Rosemary Stanton's

Great Food for Men

Dear Dad,
Lots of good recipes
for you to try...
Happy cooking
Happy Father's Day 2002.
Love us. xxx.

Rosemary Stanton's
Great Food for Men

With a foreword by Garry Egger

ALLEN&UNWIN

First published in 2002

Allen & Unwin
83 Alexander Street
Crows Nest NSW 2065
Australia
Phone: (61 2) 8425 0100
Fax: (61 2) 9906 2218
Email: frontdesk@allenandunwin.com
Web: www.allenandunwin.com

National Library of Australia
Cataloguing-in-Publication entry:

Stanton, Rosemary.
    Rosemary Stanton's great food for men.

    Includes index.
    ISBN 1 86508 708 4.

    1. Cookery. 2. Men — Nutrition. I. Title.

641.5

Designed and typeset by Nada Backovic
Photographs by Rowan Fotheringham
Food styling by Jane Hann

Set in 11 pt Fairfield
Printed by South China Printing Co. Ltd, Hong Kong

10 9 8 7 6 5 4 3 2 1

CONTENTS

FOREWORD

When I started the GutBuster program with a couple of colleagues in 1990, we had little idea of what lay ahead. It seemed like a good idea at the time, especially as we knew that about 50 per cent of men were overweight or obese and the average life expectancy for men was eight years less than for women. We also knew that few men ever went to a doctor saying, 'I've got a weight problem. It's affecting my health. Can you do something about it?' Indeed, most doctors at the time wouldn't have known what to say or do. Like Australian men, they didn't understand what was causing excess weight, much less know what to do about it.

We knew we could help if we could ever get men to admit they had a problem! The GutBuster program, which was the first of its kind in the world, struggled to keep its head above water, not because the program didn't work—it did—and because men didn't need it—they did. It struggled because of the outdated hangover from evolution that a man must never show any weakness in public. This made sense in earlier times. If you had a 'bung' leg, you never let the guy in the cave next door know because he might take advantage of it by coveting your goods and chattels.

That notion seems to have become ingrained in men. It wouldn't be considered unusual to hear about a tough Aussie farmer, accidentally cutting off his arm with a chainsaw, stopping just long enough to clean the blood off the blade. Men would find this a tale of courage. So what chance was there of a modern man turning up to a class of 'girls' to lose a bit of weight and look better. Weight Watchers has been prominent in Australia since the 1960s, but men make up only about 2 per cent of its members.

GutBusters was meant to change all that. Here was a program for men. It didn't take itself seriously. It didn't demand a drastic change in lifestyle—like giving up the grog. And it involved all the latest scientific evidence on weight loss. But men still didn't come pouring out of the woodwork to attend weight loss classes. So we tried something different and took the classes to them. In 1995 we developed an 'at-home' program with a world toll-free help line so that a bloke never had to show his face in order to lose the protuberance over his genitalia. For the first time, men started to commit. The numbers involved rose and the success stories were passed from one man to the next.

We began to find out things about men that we never knew. For example, more than 50 per cent of the men in the GutBusters program do the cooking for their family. And they not only do it, they do it well! For that reason they started to demand new and better recipes; recipes that incorporated the concepts of the GutBuster program, were low in fat, high in fibre and had flavour. They started to send their own recipes to us with great pride, and we started to put together our own little recipe book for men. Rosemary Stanton's original GutBuster cookbook was a big hit even though it looked plain and had no photographs. But men wanted more and, like women, they wanted photographs and more details about health value. Hence this newer, updated and glossier recipe book based on the principles of the

GutBuster program. There's nothing magic about these principles. They're just common sense, backed up by the latest scientific information and put into practice by Australia's best-known nutritionist. My contribution has been little, except as a taste tester. And haven't I enjoyed that! I can heartily recommend that you do the same.

If you need to capitalise on the recipes by joining up with the GutBuster program, or if you want to find out more about it, visit our website on www.gutbusters.com.au for more information.

Garry Egger

INTRODUCTION

Many top chefs are men, yet inside the home many men play a minor role in cooking. Some cook only for special occasions and enjoy this 'event cooking' when their efforts are noticed and suitably applauded. But with more women working outside the home, and a smaller percentage of people choosing traditional domestic roles, a greater number of men are taking a role in making decisions about the weekly home menu.

But not all homes include a male who can cook, and as working women have less time for shopping and cooking, many families have taken to take-away foods. Kind males noticing how tired their female partners can be after a heavy day at work may offer to assist by ducking out to buy a take-away meal. However, most of the choices available are abysmal and a disaster for the waist watcher. A typical fast food meal contains 60 or more grams of fat—more than enough for the whole day. Most also lack foods that provide fibre and have only a token slice or two of any kind of vegetable.

Some restaurants and trendy cafes offer good nutritious choices—still high in fat, but at least it's a healthier kind of fat. Such options are beyond most people's food budget for everyday eating.

In countries such as Australia, almost two-thirds of all men are overweight or obese. This is the result of too many fatty foods, many of them consumed as take-away meals, and too little exercise. The solution is to turn to home cooking with lower fat foods. If there is any argument as to who should do the cooking, it makes sense for all adults and older children living in a household to take turns. That requires ideas and recipes that are easy to put into practice. And that is the aim of this book.

Ideally, most adults who need to lose weight should aim for a total daily fat intake of 30–50 grams—less than half the current consumption in most countries. It also makes sense to increase fibre intake because fibre is filling. Aim for a total intake of 30–40 grams a day. Choosing the right breakfast cereals and breads will provide a good basis for a high fibre intake, and increasing vegetables and fruits can help too.

As well as reducing fat (especially saturated fat) and increasing fibre intake, total energy intake is also important for weight and waist loss. We get kilojoules (or calories) of energy from fats, alcohol, protein and carbohydrates. The cause of excess weight is either (a) too much fat, or (b) so many kilojoules from alcohol and carbohydrates that even a moderate intake of fat becomes superfluous and is converted to body fat.

Those who need to reduce their body fat content should therefore (a) cut down on fat (especially saturated fat) and (b) put some limits on the total quantity of kilojoules consumed. Kilojoules do count. However, it is counter-productive to cut kilojoules to the bone, as this causes the body to use less energy for its basic metabolism and makes it difficult to exercise without feeling tired. Moderate kilojoule restriction is all that is necessary—principally by cutting down on saturated fats and not overdoing alcohol and foods high in carbohydrates, especially sugar.

But all the good advice about sensible eating is useless if the food doesn't taste good. I hope you find the recipes in this book as delicious as they are nutritious.

Dr Rosemary Stanton OAM
PhD, BSc. CNutr/Diet. Grad Dip Admin. APD

BREAKFASTS

The old adage 'breakfast like a king, lunch like a queen and dine like a pauper' is a great recipe for avoiding excess body fat. Metabolism slows down overnight and it doesn't get back to full speed if you skip breakfast. Studies show that skipping breakfast reduces the metabolic rate for the whole day, thus reducing the number of kilojoules the body burns.

The ideal breakfast is often described as fresh fruit, porridge or a healthy cold cereal with fat-reduced milk, wholemeal toast with a little marmalade, jam, honey or Vegemite and something to drink (water, tea or coffee). Change the fruit according to what's in season and choose any of the quality cereals such as rolled oats (add wheatgerm for extra nutrients), Weet-Bix, Vita Brits, Sultana Bran, Soy and Linseed cereal, puffed wheat or one of the mixed flake products. Skip any that have more than 10 per cent added sugar, and if you want a toasted muesli without lots of saturated fat from coconut or 'vegetable oil', make your own (see recipe). If your tastes and lifestyle fit better with a breakfast of rice and vegetables or lean steak and tomatoes, that's fine.

For most people needing to lose weight, breakfast should contain no more than 8–10 grams of fat and about 1300–1500 kJ.

TIPS

Three easy, healthy, low-fat cooked breakfasts to serve on toast:

- grilled mushrooms and tomatoes
- hot canned creamed corn
- baked beans

If you're not hungry at breakfast, get up a few minutes earlier and go for a swim or a walk to stimulate your metabolism and appetite.

If you're short of time at breakfast, make a quick smoothie or grab a bread roll and wrap it round a banana and eat it on the way to work or school.

If you can't help missing breakfast occasionally, make yourself a healthy mid-morning snack of low-fat yoghurt with fruit or have rye crispbread with ricotta and tomato or banana.

DRIED FRUITS WITH YOGHURT

This recipe will keep for several days in the refrigerator.

1. Place the orange juice, water and dried fruit into a large saucepan. Bring to the boil, cover and simmer for 10 minutes. Serve warm or chill in the fridge until required.

   For a complete quick breakfast, serve with a carton (200 g) low-fat yoghurt.

500 mL orange juice
500 mL water
400 g dried fruit medley
   (sultanas, peaches,
   pears, apricots,
   apples)
½ cup dried apples

PER SERVE: 0 G FAT, 5 G DIETARY FIBRE, 900 KJ (215 CALS)

WITH YOGHURT, PER SERVE: 1 G FAT, 5 G DIETARY FIBRE, 1340 KJ (320 CALS)

 SERVES 6

Toasted Muesli

Most commercial toasted mueslis are made by soaking the ingredients in a mixture of sugar and saturated vegetable or coconut fat, then baking or frying the lot. The only fat in this delicious recipe is the healthy unsaturated kind from seeds and nuts. It doesn't need any added sugar.

750 g rolled oats
250 g rye or barley
    flakes*
¼ cup sesame seeds
½ cup flaked almonds
1 cup wheatgerm
200 g dried fruit medley
    (sultanas, peaches,
    pears, apricots,
    apples)
250 g sultanas
½ cup pepitas*
1 cup sunflower seeds
½ cup roasted
    buckwheat*

** available from the
health food section of
the supermarket*

 **MAKES 32 x 60 G
SERVINGS**

1. Preheat the oven to 180°C. Spread half the oats and rye or barley flakes on an ungreased oven tray and bake for about 10–15 minutes, stirring several times until the oats are golden brown (take care they don't burn). Spread onto a large plate or tray to cool. Repeat with the rest of the oats and rye or barley.
2. Toast the sesame seeds and almonds by the same method, checking after 3–5 minutes. Cool.
3. Combine the oats, seeds and nuts with the remaining ingredients, mixing well. Store in an airtight container.

PER SERVE: 7 G FAT, 5 G DIETARY FIBRE, 930 KJ (225 CALS)
WITH 1/2 CUP FAT-REDUCED MILK, PER SERVE: 9 G FAT, 5 G DIETARY FIBRE, 1185 KJ (285 CALS)

SWISS MUESLI

True Swiss muesli is not a dry cereal that comes in a packet, but is partly prepared the night before. Try it, it's excellent.

1. In a bowl, combine the oats, milk and honey. Leave in the refrigerator overnight.
2. Just before serving, add the apples, hazelnuts and yoghurt.

Tip: For extra flavour, toast the hazelnuts for a couple of minutes in a dry frying pan over a medium heat. Cool before using.

PER SERVE: 8 G FAT, 5 G DIETARY FIBRE, 1190 KJ (285 CALS)

1 ½ cups rolled oats
1 cup skim milk
1 tbsp honey
2 apples, cored
  and grated
¼ cup chopped
  hazelnuts
200 g low-fat yoghurt

 SERVES 4

BANANA SMOOTHIE

Ideal for a quick breakfast when you are running late.

1 banana
100 g low-fat
  natural yoghurt
½ cup skim milk
1 tsp of honey
2 tsp wheatgerm
2 ice blocks

1. Place all the ingredients in a blender, process until smooth and frothy.

PER SERVE: 2 G FAT, 3 G DIETARY FIBRE, 965 KJ (230 CALS)

 SERVES 1

ROCKMELON SOY SMOOTHIE

Another quick breakfast-in-a-glass.

*1 slice chilled
    rockmelon (about
    125 g), peeled
    and seeded
1 cup fat-free
    soy beverage
1 tsp honey
100 g low-fat yoghurt*

1. Place all the ingredients in a blender, process until smooth and frothy.

PER SERVE: 0 G FAT, 1 G DIETARY FIBRE, 850 KJ (205 CALS)

 SERVES 1

STRAWBERRY PEAR SMOOTHIE

A fast and delicious breakfast.

1. Place all the ingredients in a blender, and process until smooth and frothy.

PER SERVE: 1 G FAT, 6 G DIETARY FIBRE, 1020 KJ (245 CALS)

*½ punnet of
    strawberries
1 medium pear,
    peeled and cored
¾ cup skim milk
100 g low-fat fruit
    yoghurt*

 SERVES 1

ROCKMELON SOY SMOOTHIE — SEE PAGE 6

TOASTED MUESLI — SEE PAGE 4

OAT BRAN MINI PANCAKES

These healthy mini pancakes are great for a weekend breakfast. Don't try to make large pancakes as the mixture is too light to flip them successfully.

1. Place all the ingredients in a blender or food processor and process until smooth. Leave the mixture to stand for 30 minutes, or refrigerate overnight.
2. Heat a frying pan and spray with light olive oil. Pour enough of the mixture into the frying pan to form mini pancakes about 5 cm in diameter. Cook over a moderate heat until golden brown, flip and brown the other side. Repeat with the remaining mixture. Serve with lemon juice and fresh strawberries or stewed or canned fruit.

PER SERVE: 5 G FAT, 6 G DIETARY FIBRE, 760 KJ (180 CALS)

¾ cup oat bran
1 ½ cups buttermilk
1 egg
½ cup wholemeal
*   plain flour*
¼ tsp bicarbonate of
*   soda*
2 tsp sugar
light olive oil spray

 SERVES 4

FRENCH TOAST

For something different, make French toast with fruit loaf.

For each person
½ cup skim milk
pinch cinnamon
½ tsp finely chopped
    lemon rind
1 egg
2 slices fruit loaf
light olive oil spray
1 tsp sugar

 **MAKES 2 SLICES,
SERVES 1**

1. Beat together the milk, cinnamon, rind and egg. Dip each slice of bread into the mixture, moving it with a fork so the bread soaks up the milk.
2. Heat a non-stick frying pan, spray with light olive oil spray and cook the toast until brown on both sides. Sprinkle with sugar and serve immediately.

PER SERVE: 7 G FAT, 2 G DIETARY FIBRE, 1280 KJ (305 CALS)

CARROT AND ORANGE MUFFINS

These muffins have a great flavour and are excellent for hungry people at breakfast or brunch. Use a food processor to grate the carrot and then mix the ingredients.

1. Preheat oven to 190°C and spray 6 large or 12 small non-stick muffin pans with light olive oil spray.
2. Grate the carrot and mix with the juice, eggs, honey, oil and cinnamon.
3. Add the sifted flour and baking powder, taking care not to over-mix. Spoon into muffin pans and bake for 25 minutes. Serve warm.

PER SERVE (1 LARGE MUFFIN): 6 G FAT, 6 G DIETARY FIBRE, 970 KJ (230 CALS)

PER SERVE (1 SMALL MUFFIN): 3 G FAT, 3 G DIETARY FIBRE, 485 KJ (115 CALS)

light olive oil spray
1 large carrot (about 150 g), grated
1 cup orange juice
2 eggs
2 tbsp honey, preferably leatherwood
1 tbsp macadamia (or light olive) oil
1 tsp cinnamon
2 cups wholemeal self-raising flour
¾ tsp baking powder

MAKES 6 LARGE OR 12 SMALL MUFFINS

LUNCHTIME SANDWICHES

Lord Sandwich hated meals to interrupt his gambling, so he ordered his dinner to be placed between two slices of bread and brought to the gaming table, thus inventing the sandwich. If you work near a good sandwich shop, you may be able to choose an excellent lunch each day, although you'll need to avoid mayonnaise as it has heaps of fat. If the only choices available are meat pies, sausage rolls, chips or some kind of fast food, plan ahead and take your lunch with you. Try sandwiches, soups—hot in winter, chilled in summer (see pages 57–75)—and hearty salads for a delicious healthy lunch. Add some fruit and iced water and you have an easy, low-fat meal.

TIPS

Freeze a small bottle of water. Pack it next to sandwiches and other lunch ingredients and it will keep the lunch cool. You can also enjoy the cold water as a drink.

For lunch on the run, grab a couple of bread rolls, a small tin of tuna and a tomato. Add fresh fruit.

Vary the bread you use at lunchtime. Try white high fibre, white crusty, wholemeal, multigrain, soy and linseed, dark or regular rye, rolls of all shapes, bagels, pita, half rounds of Lebanese bread, lavash (also known as mountain bread) and even tortillas or Indian breads like roti (check the label and choose those with less than 2 g fat/100 g or look for no form of fat in the ingredient list).

Keep a packet of rice paper wraps at work. Reconstitute then by soaking in water for 3 or 4 minutes. Wrap them round some Thai salad from a fresh take-away bar.

Buy sushi or sashimi for lunch. They have virtually no fat.

EASY, EVERYDAY FRESH SANDWICHES

These easy sandwiches all provide a fast, healthy lunch.

CHEESE AND SALAD
Start with wholegrain bread, add sliced reduced-fat cheddar (7 per cent fat) and top with lettuce, grated fresh beetroot and carrot, sliced capsicum and another slice of wholegrain bread.

PER SERVE: 4 G FAT, 7 G DIETARY FIBRE, 930 KJ (220 CALS)

HAM AND POTATO SALAD
Fill a pita bread with shaved lean ham, tomato and potato and chick pea salad (see page 22).

PER SERVE: 3 G FAT, 4 G DIETARY FIBRE, 1015 KJ (245 CALS)

MINTED EGG AND LETTUCE
Stuff a wholemeal roll with egg, chopped mint and shredded lettuce.

PER SERVE: 7 G FAT, 5 G DIETARY FIBRE, 885 KJ (210 CALS)

SALMON, CUCUMBER AND OLIVE
Start with 2 slices of good crusty Italian bread and fill with 100 g canned skinless salmon, thinly sliced cucumber and sliced black olives.

PER SERVE: 7 G FAT, 3 G DIETARY FIBRE, 1335 KJ (320 CALS)

SARDINES, LEMON AND LETTUCE
Split a multigrain bread roll and add a small can of well-drained sardines, thin slices of lemon and lettuce. (Take the ingredients and put your sandwich together when you're ready for lunch.)

PER SERVE: 14 G FAT (ALL 'GOOD' FAT), 5 G DIETARY FIBRE, 1300 KJ (310 CALS)

ROAST LAMB AND MINT JELLY
Use light rye bread and fill with roast lamb, mint jelly and a couple of sliced raw button mushrooms.

PER SERVE: 6 G FAT, 4 G DIETARY FIBRE, 1275 KJ (305 CALS)

AVOCADO AND SALAD
Start with wholegrain dark rye bread, spread one slice with avocado and top with lettuce, slices of cucumber, sliced cold potato, snow pea sprouts and another slice of bread.

PER SERVE: 13 G FAT ('GOOD' FAT), 9 G DIETARY FIBRE, 1445 KJ (345 CALS)

SANDWICHES WITH A DIFFERENCE

Simple ideas, but different enough to prevent lunch becoming boring.

CHICKEN AND MANGO CHUTNEY

Start with lavash bread, top with sliced chicken breast, sliced fresh ginger, a spoonful of mango chutney and some mung bean sprouts and wrap it up.

PER SERVE: 6 G FAT, 3 G DIETARY FIBRE, 1425 KJ (340 CALS)

SPICY PUMPKIN

Sprinkle chunks of pumpkin with cumin and roast them in a moderate oven (do this with the previous night's dinner), top with a tablespoon of low-fat yoghurt mixed with a teaspoon of tahini and serve in pita bread.

PER SERVE: 6 G FAT, 4 G DIETARY FIBRE, 1075 KJ (255 CALS)

MUSHROOM AND TUNA

Wrap mushroom and tuna salad (see page 26) in lavash bread.

PER SERVE: 7 G FAT, 4 G DIETARY FIBRE, 1130 KJ (270 CALS)

BEEF WITH HORSERADISH

Take a chunk of French stick, split it and fill with 2 slices of rare roast beef topped with beetroot and horseradish salad (see page 23).

PER SERVE: 5 G FAT, 4 G DIETARY FIBRE, 1130 KJ (270 CALS)

TABBOULI AND BEETROOT

Stuff pita bread or a piece of Turkish bread with tabbouli (see page 30) and sliced beetroot.

PER SERVE: 3 G FAT, 6 G DIETARY FIBRE, 1090 KJ (260 CALS)

RICOTTA AND SALAD

Start with split Turkish bread, spread with low-fat ricotta cheese and add baby spinach leaves, sliced tomatoes and black olives.

PER SERVE: 8 G FAT, 4 G DIETARY FIBRE, 1240 KJ (295 CALS)

INDIAN SPECIAL

Take leftover chunks of baked vegetables, toss them with a spoonful of tikka curry paste, spoon onto an Indian roti, add a little mango chutney and fold over.

SMOKED SALMON

Spread wholemeal bread with low-fat ricotta cheese and top with smoked salmon, capers and sliced cucumber.

PER SERVE: 8 G FAT, 4 G DIETARY FIBRE, 1385 KJ (330 CALS)

SWEET BAGEL

Toast a bagel, split it, spread with light spreadable cream cheese, and top with chopped dried apricots, toasted almonds and a sprinkle of cinnamon.

PER SERVE: 9 G FAT, 5 G DIETARY FIBRE, 1400 KJ (335 CALS)

BRUSCHETTA

Take thick slices of Italian bread, rub with a cut clove of garlic, toast and top with thick slices of ripe tomato, some fresh basil and a few drops of extra virgin olive oil.

PER SERVE: 6 G FAT, 5 G DIETARY FIBRE, 1100 KJ (260 CALS)

SANDWICHES TO FREEZE

If you're too rushed to make lunch each day, get some good bread (preferably wholegrain, rye, soy and linseed or Turkish), make enough sandwiches to last during the following week and freeze them. Not all fillings freeze well, but the following are excellent. (Fat, fibre and kilojoule counts assume wholemeal bread and average quantities of each filling.)

- Chicken or turkey with cranberry sauce

  PER SERVE: 4 G FAT, 4 G DIETARY FIBRE, 970 KJ (230 CALS)

- Lean roast beef and mustard

  PER SERVE: 5 G FAT, 4 G DIETARY FIBRE, 970 KJ (230 CALS)

- Roast pork with apple sauce

  PER SERVE: 5 G FAT, 4 G DIETARY FIBRE, 1010 KJ (240 CALS)

- Roast veal and mango chutney

  PER SERVE: 3 G FAT, 4 G DIETARY FIBRE, 1010 KJ (240 CALS)

- Cold sliced roast pumpkin with toasted sunflower seeds

  PER SERVE: 7 G FAT, 5 G DIETARY FIBRE, 900 KJ (215 CALS)

- Sliced leftover boiled potatoes, ham and pickles

  PER SERVE: 4 G FAT, 5 G DIETARY FIBRE, 1000 KJ (240 CALS)

- Hard boiled egg, chopped and combined with parsley and a little natural yoghurt

  PER SERVE: 7 G FAT, 4 G DIETARY FIBRE, 860 KJ (205 CALS)

- Potato salad (use low-fat yoghurt instead of mayonnaise in the dressing)

  PER SERVE: 2 G FAT, 5 G DIETARY FIBRE, 750 KJ (180 CALS)

- Low-fat hummus and sun-dried tomatoes (reconstitute dried tomatoes by placing them in a small bowl or a cup, just cover with boiling water and leave for 15 minutes before draining and cutting into pieces)

  PER SERVE: 6 G FAT, 7 G DIETARY FIBRE, 970 KJ (230 CALS)

- Canned tuna with sliced water chestnuts

  PER SERVE: 3 G FAT, 4 G DIETARY FIBRE, 920 KJ (220 CALS)

- Canned salmon and sliced celery

  PER SERVE: 7 G FAT, 4 G DIETARY FIBRE, 1000 KJ (240 CALS)

- Dried fruit with sliced ginger and a few walnuts

  PER SERVE: 7 G FAT, 8 G DIETARY FIBRE, 1340 KJ (320 CALS)

SALADS

Salads were once predictable and boring. Not any more. The wide variety of salads now enjoyed are great for lunch, a light evening meal or even as a first course at dinner. Many also travel well, making them ideal to take to work or out on a picnic, especially if you take the dressing in a small jar and add it just before serving. Try to get good extra virgin olive oil for a salad. Although olive oil has just as many kilojoules as any other oil, you can get flavour for minimum kilojoules with a quality oil.

TIPS

Buy a good quality extra virgin olive oil for salads because its strong flavour (and price) means you won't use too much. A tossed green salad for two people needs no more than 1 tablespoon of dressing. Toss it well and you'll find it's enough.

A squeeze of lemon juice is good on many salads, or try mixing 1 teaspoon of mild prepared mustard with 1 tablespoon of lemon juice.

Cucumber and yoghurt dressing is excellent with chargrilled zucchini slices or potato salad. Use 1–2 grated Lebanese cucumbers, some chopped mint and a tablespoon of lemon juice with 200 g low-fat yoghurt.

Char grill asparagus spears, whole green beans, sliced eggplant, zucchini or quartered capsicums, small halved onions, halved heads of garlic or sliced pumpkin to make salads more interesting.

Try different vinegars on salads: balsamic, raspberry, cider, or herb and mustard vinegars all add flavour without kilojoules.

Add watercress and rocket to salad greens to give more flavour.

Grow your own salad vegetables. Perpetual spinach and Asian greens available at plant nurseries can be grown in pots and picked just before dinner.

ITALIAN BREAD AND TOMATO SALAD

This is a great salad to make when you're home for lunch because it's best eaten soon after it's been made. It is excellent with barbecued chicken breast, fish or lean grilled lamb.

1. Preheat the oven to 180°C. Slice the bread about twice the thickness of regular sliced bread and bake in the prepared oven for about 15 minutes, or until the bread browns and is crisp. Cool a little and then break into chunks, about 1.5 cm square.
2. Combine the bread with the remaining ingredients. Toss well and eat within about 30 minutes.

PER SERVE: 6 G FAT, 4 G DIETARY FIBRE, 800 KJ (190 CALS)

½ a small loaf of crusty Italian bread (approx 200 g)
500 g ripe tomatoes, cut into chunks
1 clove garlic, crushed
1 small onion, peeled and diced
½ cup chopped parsley
1 tbsp extra virgin olive oil
freshly ground black pepper

 SERVES 4

WARM BARBECUED VEGETABLE SALAD

If you double this recipe, the leftovers make an excellent filling for pita bread for lunch the next day.

1 eggplant, about 500 g, cut into 8 slices
4 zucchini, sliced lengthwise
olive oil spray
1 red capsicum, seeded and sliced
8 egg tomatoes, halved lengthwise
1 cup tomato pasta sauce
1 tbsp balsamic vinegar
½ cup chopped fresh basil

1. Heat the barbecue. Spray the eggplant and zucchini with the olive oil spray and barbecue for about 10 minutes, turning once, or until the vegetables are cooked.
2. Arrange the eggplant, zucchini, capsicum and tomatoes on a serving platter.
3. Heat the pasta sauce and add the vinegar. Drizzle over the vegetables and sprinkle with basil. Serve warm.

PER SERVE: 3 G FAT, 9 G DIETARY FIBRE, 460 KJ (110 CALS)

SERVES 4

CHEESE AND GREENS SALAD

This is a good lunch to have on weekends. If baby spinach is not available, use rocket or any kind of lettuce.

1 bunch fresh asparagus
1 small wholemeal
    French stick
100 g reduced-fat
    cheddar (7 per
    cent fat)
2 cups baby spinach
    leaves
mixed lettuces (for
    example, cos, coral,
    mignonette, butter,
    oak leaf, mustard,
    rocket)
watercress

Dressing
2 tbsp extra virgin
    olive oil
2 tbsp balsamic vinegar
1 tsp Dijon mustard

 SERVES 4

1. Cook the asparagus in boiling water for 2 minutes, drain immediately and place into a bowl of cold water to cool and keep it green. Drain.
2. Preheat the oven to 180°C. Cut the French stick into 4 thick diagonal slices and place a quarter of the cheese on each slice. Bake for 12–15 minutes or until the edges of the bread are crusty.
3. Combine the dressing ingredients.
4. Arrange the salad leaves and asparagus on four individual plates. Drizzle the dressing over the leaves and top with the cheese toast. Serve at once.

PER SERVE: 13 G FAT, 7 G DIETARY FIBRE, 1200 KJ (285 CALS)

PUMPKIN SALAD WITH SEEDS

Bake extra pumpkin the night before and keep it for this delicious salad. It is excellent rolled up in lavash or mountain bread.

1. Preheat the oven to 180°C. Place the pumpkin on an oven tray and coat lightly with olive oil spray. Bake for about 15 minutes, or until just tender. Set aside to cool.
2. Combine the cooked pumpkin with the sprouts and rocket.
3. For the dressing, toast the pepitas and the sunflower seeds in a dry frying pan over a gentle heat until golden brown (take care they do not burn). Gently heat the remaining dressing ingredients in a small saucepan, stirring until the honey dissolves. Sprinkle the dressing over the pumpkin and toss lightly together. Top with the toasted seeds.

PER SERVE: 10 G FAT, 4 G DIETARY FIBRE, 920 KJ (220 CALS)

750 g pumpkin (preferably butternut), peeled, seeded and cut into chunks
olive oil spray
1 punnet sunflower sprouts
½ bunch rocket

Dressing
1 tbsp pepitas (green pumpkin seeds)
1 tbsp sunflower seeds
1 tbsp extra virgin olive oil
1 tbsp cider vinegar
1 tbsp white wine vinegar
1 tsp honey

 SERVES 4

POTATO AND CHICK PEA SALAD

This is a hearty filling salad which is great to take to work for lunch.

500 g small new potatoes

½ cup frozen peas,
   defrosted

400 g can chick peas,
   drained

1 red capsicum,
   seeded and diced

1 cup sliced celery

½ cup chopped
   Italian parsley

2 tbsp balsamic vinegar

½ cup low-fat yoghurt

1. Microwave or steam the potatoes until tender.
2. Cut the potatoes in half and combine with the peas, chick peas, capsicum and celery. Leave for 10 minutes.
3. Add the parsley, vinegar and yoghurt to the potatoes and toss well to combine. If not serving straight away, cover and keep in the fridge.

PER SERVE: 2 G FAT, 8 G DIETARY FIBRE, 760 KJ (180 CALS)

 SERVES 4

GREEN BEAN SALAD WITH AVOCADO DRESSING

Serve with Turkish bread, or as part of a main meal with barbecued chicken or fish.

1. Steam the beans for 2 minutes (they should still be crisp). Drain and place immediately into a large bowl of cold water to stop the cooking process and keep the beans crisp and green. Drain.
2. Place the dressing ingredients into a blender and process until thick and smooth.
3. Toss the beans with the capsicum and top with the dressing.

PER SERVE: 9 G FAT, 5 G DIETARY FIBRE, 620 KJ (150 CALS)

500 g green beans, trimmed

1 red capsicum,
   seeded and sliced

Dressing

½ ripe avocado

2 tsp French mustard

100 g low-fat ricotta cheese

100 g low-fat natural
   yoghurt

2 tbsp lemon juice

 SERVES 4

POTATO AND CHICK PEA SALAD — SEE PAGE 22

ASIAN BEAN AND NOODLE SALAD — SEE PAGE 28

MINTED BEAN SALAD

Beans are high in protein, vitamins, minerals and fibre, and have virtually no fat. This hearty salad is excellent to take to work for lunch.

1. Combine all the ingredients and refrigerate for at least 30 minutes to allow the flavours to mingle.

PER SERVE: 5 G FAT, 9 G DIETARY FIBRE, 660 KJ (160 CALS)

680 g can four bean
  mix, drained
1 punnet cherry tomatoes
2 Lebanese
  cucumbers, diced
½ cup sliced green shallots
100 g sliced mushrooms
½ cup chopped mint
2 tbsp lemon juice
1 tbsp olive or
  macadamia nut oil
freshly ground black pepper

 SERVES 4

BEETROOT AND HORSERADISH SALAD

This easy to make salad goes well with lean roast beef and a crusty bread roll. Use a food processor to make grating easier.

4 medium-sized
  fresh beetroot
2–3 tsp grated
  horseradish (or 1
  tbsp prepared
  creamed horseradish)
2 tbsp wine vinegar
freshly ground
  black pepper

1. Peel the beetroot (wear gloves if you don't want stained hands). Remove the tops and root. Grate coarsely.
2. Combine the beetroot with the horseradish, vinegar and pepper. Stand for at least 15 minutes to allow the flavours to blend.

PER SERVE: 1 G FAT, 18 G DIETARY FIBRE, 1000 KJ (240 CALS)

SERVES 4

WARM SPICED PEAR SALAD WITH ROCKET AND WALNUTS

This is an excellent salad as a first course at a dinner party. Sumac (a Middle Eastern spice mix) is available from spice shops and most delicatessens.

1 tbsp walnuts

olive oil spray

2 tsp sumac

1 tsp cinnamon

1 tsp ground cumin

4 firm pears, peeled and cored

½ cup orange juice

2 tbsp lemon juice

1 tbsp wholegrain mustard

2 tsp Dijon-style mustard

1 tsp honey

1 bunch rocket, ends trimmed

1. Toast the walnuts in a dry frying pan over moderate heat for 2–3 minutes or until they are golden brown. Tip onto a plate to cool.
2. Preheat the oven to 200°C and spray a medium-sized baking dish with the olive oil.
3. Combine the sumac, cinnamon and cumin. Place the pears and orange juice into a bowl and sprinkle with the spices, tossing gently. Tip the pears into the baking dish and bake for 10 minutes, turning once.
4. While the pears are cooking, combine the lemon juice, mustards and honey, stirring well to dissolve the honey.
5. Arrange the rocket on serving plates, top with the warm pears and drizzle with dressing.

PER SERVE: 4 G FAT, 6 G DIETARY FIBRE, 690 KJ (165 CALS)

 SERVES 4

Salmon pasta salad

Try different coloured pasta to make this salad look attractive.

1. Cook the pasta according to the directions on the packet. Drain well.
2. Steam the broccoli for 2–3 minutes or microwave for 1–2 minutes. Drain and place immediately into a large bowl or basin of cold water to stop the cooking process. Drain.
3. In a salad bowl, combine the cooked pasta, broccoli, mushrooms, celery, capsicums, tomatoes and salmon.
4. For the dressing, combine the yoghurt, lemon juice, chives, coriander, paprika and mustard. Pour over pasta and mix well.

Per serve: 7 g fat, 9 g dietary fibre, 1470 kJ (350 Cals)

200 g spiral pasta
250 g broccoli florets
100 g button mushrooms, sliced
2 stalks celery, sliced
1 red capsicum, seeded and diced
1 green capsicum, seeded and diced
1 punnet cherry tomatoes
220 g can red salmon, flaked

Dressing
200 g low-fat natural yoghurt
2 tbsp lemon juice
1 tbsp chopped chives
½ cup chopped fresh coriander (or use parsley)
1 tsp paprika
1 tbsp wholegrain mustard

 SERVES 4

MUSHROOM AND TUNA SALAD

Make this salad at least 30 minutes before you want to eat so the mushrooms can absorb some of the flavours.

1 tbsp lemon juice

2 tsp olive oil

2 tsp balsamic vinegar
  (or use wine vinegar)

2 tsp wholegrain
  mustard

1 tsp castor sugar

freshly ground pepper

200 g button
  mushrooms, sliced

100 g can tuna in
  spring water

1 tbsp chopped chives

6 green shallots, sliced

 SERVES 2

1. Combine the lemon juice, oil, vinegar, mustard, sugar and pepper.
2. Add the mushrooms and undrained tuna and toss lightly but thoroughly. Top with the chives and shallots, cover with plastic wrap and refrigerate for at least 30 minutes. Mix well just before serving.

PER SERVE: 6 G FAT, 3 G DIETARY FIBRE, 605 KJ (145 CALS)

GREEN SALAD WITH POTATOES, EGG DRESSING AND CRISP CROUTONS

Cook some extra potatoes the night before to use in this salad. Including bread and potatoes makes this less like rabbit food!

1. Preheat the oven to 180°C. Place the bread on an oven tray and spray both sides of each slice with olive oil. Bake in the prepared oven for 15–20 minutes, or until the bread is crisp and brown.
2. Place the salad leaves, rocket and potatoes in a salad bowl.
3. Make the dressing by heating lemon juice, vinegar, water and mustard in a small saucepan. Whisk the egg in a small bowl until frothy and add the hot lemon mixture, whisking continuously until well combined. Return the mixture to the saucepan and stir over a very low heat until hot. Do not boil or the dressing will curdle. Add the pepper to the dressing and pour over the salad. Toss well and serve at once.

PER SERVE: 4 G FAT, 6 G DIETARY FIBRE, 770 KJ (185 CALS)

3 slices bread,
  crusts removed
olive oil spray
6–8 cups mixed lettuce
  (iceberg, oak leaf,
  butter, radicchio or
  any other available
  lettuces)
1 bunch rocket, washed
  and dried
8 small new potatoes,
  steamed and cut
  into quarters

Dressing
2 tbsp lemon juice
2 tbsp white
  wine vinegar
2 tbsp water
1 tbsp prepared
  Dijon mustard
1 egg
freshly ground
  black pepper

 SERVES 4

ASIAN BEAN AND NOODLE SALAD

Lots of flavour in this Thai-style salad.

125 g rice noodles

60 g unsalted peanuts

250 g green beans,
briefly steamed

100 g snow peas, sliced

170 g can water
chestnuts, drained
and sliced

250 g mung bean sprouts

½ small Chinese
cabbage, shredded
finely

½ cup chopped mint,
including some
Vietnamese mint if
available

1 cup coriander sprigs

2 or 3 fresh lime leaves,
rib removed and
shredded very finely

2 tsp chopped chilli
(optional)

Dressing

2 tsp palm sugar (or use
dark brown sugar)

¼ cup rice vinegar

2 tbsp lime juice

1 tbsp fish sauce

1. Prepare the rice noodles according to the instructions on the packet. Rinse with cold water, separating the noodles with your fingers. Drain well.

2. Toast the peanuts in a dry frying pan over a medium heat, shaking often until they brown. Tip onto a plate to cool.

3. Place the rice noodles, beans, snow peas, water chestnuts, sprouts, cabbage, mint, coriander, lime leaves and chilli (if used) into a large bowl.

4. Combine all the ingredients for the dressing, pour over the salad and toss well. Just before serving, top with the peanuts.

PER SERVE: 5 G FAT, 7 G DIETARY FIBRE, 770 KJ (185 CALS)

 SERVES 6

GREEK SALAD

Low-fat fetta cheese has only 3 per cent fat and is now available in supermarkets. It crumbles well and adds loads of flavour.

1. Place the tomatoes, cucumber, onion, lettuce, parsley and cheese into a salad bowl.
2. Combine the olive oil and lemon juice and pour over the salad, tossing well to mix thoroughly. Top with the olives.

PER SERVE: 7 G FAT, 6 G DIETARY FIBRE, 570 KJ (135 CALS)

4 medium-sized
tomatoes, cored
and diced
2 Lebanese cucumbers,
cut into chunks
1 small purple onion,
sliced
half an iceberg lettuce,
cut into chunks
½ cup parsley sprigs
100 g crumbled
fetta cheese
½ cup (60 g)
black olives

Dressing
1 tbsp olive oil
1 tbsp lemon juice

 SERVES 4

TABBOULI LIME SALAD

Quick and easy, this salad will keep for a day or two in the fridge. It is especially good packed into wholemeal pita bread.

1 cup cracked wheat
   (burghul)
2 cups boiling water
3 cups chopped
   Italian parsley
½ cup finely
   chopped mint
6 green shallots, sliced
¼ cup lime juice
1 tbsp extra virgin
   olive oil
freshly ground
   black pepper
1 Lebanese cucumber,
   diced
1 punnet cherry
   tomatoes, halved
   (if large)

 SERVES 6

1. Place the cracked wheat in a saucepan or a bowl and pour the boiling water over it. Cover and leave to stand for 15 minutes (the wheat will absorb the water).
2. Fluff up the wheat with a fork and add the parsley, mint, shallots, lime juice, olive oil and pepper. Stir gently and leave for 15 minutes.
3. Add the cucumber and tomatoes.

PER SERVE: 4 G FAT, 5 G DIETARY FIBRE, 525 KJ (125 CALS)

PINEAPPLE COLESLAW

Use a food processor for fast slicing.

1. Place the pineapple, cabbage, capsicum, carrot and fennel in a large bowl and mix gently together.
2. Combine the dressing ingredients and stir well. Pour over the cabbage mix and toss well to combine.

PER SERVE: 1 G FAT, 9 G DIETARY FIBRE, 470 KJ (110 CALS)

2 slices fresh pineapple,
  chopped
6 cups shredded
  cabbage
1 green capsicum,
  seeded and sliced
1 red capsicum
1 large carrot, grated
1 small head fennel,
  sliced finely

Dressing
3 tbsp lemon juice
½ cup chopped mint
200 g low-fat natural
  yoghurt

SERVES 4

GRAINS

PASTA, NOODLES, RICE, POLENTA, COUSCOUS, BARLEY, BUCKWHEAT

Grains contribute complex carbohydrates, fibre and very little fat to our diet, but their nutritional value is often ruined with added fat. It doesn't have to be that way, as these recipes show. Noodles and pasta are now made from wheat, buckwheat, corn, rice or mung bean flours. Some have a mixture of grains and some include egg. If you have a wheat allergy, check the label of any product carefully, as noodles made primarily of corn or rice may sometimes include some wheat.

TIPS

To skin tomatoes for a pasta sauce, remove the core and plunge the tomatoes into the boiling pasta water. After 30 seconds lift out with a slotted spoon. The skin will slip off easily.

Instead of cream in a pasta sauce, use low-fat evaporated milk. It doesn't taste as good, but it's a reasonable second best.

Cook pasta only to the *al dente* stage (literally 'to the tooth') as it will create a lower glycaemic load within the body. This means it will be digested slowly and provide energy over a longer period compared with pasta that is cooked until it is soggy. Start testing pasta by tasting a piece 2 minutes before the stated cooking time.

Buy dried tomatoes from the vegetable section of the supermarket rather than those in jars of oil. To reconstitute dried tomatoes, place in a small bowl, cover with boiling water and leave for 15 minutes. Drain and reserve the liquid to use in soups or sauces.

To cook pasta successfully, you need lots of boiling water—almost a litre for each 100 g of pasta.

Unless you're making a pasta salad, don't try to drain off every last bit of water. A little water clinging to hot pasta helps the sauce adhere. Don't add oil to the pasta water as the sauce won't stick to the pasta.

FETTUCCINE WITH PUMPKIN, SPINACH AND SUNFLOWER SEEDS

English spinach gives a better result than silver beet.

1. Toast the sunflower seeds in a dry frying pan, shaking often until they are golden brown, taking care they don't burn. Set aside.
2. Cook the fettuccine according to packet directions.
3. While the fettuccine is cooking, heat the oil in a non-stick frying pan and cook the onion, garlic and thyme over a gentle heat for 3–4 minutes, stirring several times. Add the pumpkin and continue cooking for another 3–4 minutes, turning the pumpkin slices so they soften but don't become mushy.
4. Trim the stalks from the spinach, wash and add the leaves to the frying pan. Cover and cook for 1–2 minutes until the spinach wilts.
5. Drain the fettuccine and serve topped with the pumpkin and spinach mixture. Sprinkle each bowl with sunflower seeds and the cheese.

2 tbsp sunflower seeds
400 g spinach fettuccine
2 tsp olive oil
1 medium onion,
  sliced finely
2 cloves garlic, crushed
1 tsp dried thyme
about 400 g butternut
  pumpkin, sliced finely
1 bunch English spinach
1 tbsp grated Parmesan

PER SERVE: 9 G FAT, 8 G DIETARY FIBRE, 1980 KJ (470 CALS)

 SERVES 4

PASTA WITH LEMON, ROCKET, ROSEMARY AND CAPERS

A simple dish that is ideal if you have had a big lunch.

375 g pasta shells
2 tsp olive oil
2 cloves garlic, crushed
finely grated peel and
  juice of 1 lemon
2 tbsp finely chopped
  fresh rosemary
1 tbsp capers
1 bunch rocket, washed
2 tbsp Parmesan cheese

1. Cook the pasta according to packet directions. Drain when cooked.
2. While the pasta is cooking, heat a frying pan and add the oil, garlic, lemon peel and rosemary. Cook over a gentle heat for 1 minute. Add the capers and rocket and heat until the rocket wilts.
3. Add the lemon juice to the cooked pasta and toss well, then add the rocket mixture and toss to combine. Serve sprinkled with the Parmesan.

PER SERVE: 6 G FAT, 6 G DIETARY FIBRE, 1620 KJ (385 CALS)

SERVES 4

ROAST VEGETABLE LASAGNE

This is a good dish to prepare ahead. If you can't get fresh lasagne, use instant dried lasagne and soften each sheet in a large bowl of hot water for 2 minutes before using.

1 tbsp olive oil

6 medium onions,
 peeled and cut into
 eight wedges

6 cloves garlic, unpeeled

1 large orange sweet
 potato, about 500 g,
 peeled and diced into
 2 cm pieces

2 red capsicums,
 seeded and each
 cut into 8 pieces

1 green capsicum,
 seeded and cut into
 8 pieces

400 g fresh
 button mushrooms

2 tbsp balsamic vinegar

6 fresh lasagne sheets
 (about 280 g)

250 g frozen
 spinach, defrosted

250 g fat-reduced ricotta

2 x 400 g can
 crushed tomatoes

cooking foil

2 tbsp grated Parmesan

1. Preheat the oven to 200°C. Place a 20 cm x 28 cm baking dish into the oven for 2 minutes to heat. Remove the baking dish and add the oil, onions, garlic, sweet potato, capsicums and mushrooms, shaking the vegetables to coat them with the oil. Drizzle the balsamic vinegar over the vegetables and roast for 30 minutes, turning once.

2. Remove the garlic cloves and tip the roasted vegetables into a large bowl. When the garlic is cool enough to handle, squeeze out the flesh and add it to the roasted vegetables, tossing gently.

3. Spoon the vegetables into a large ovenproof dish and place the lasagne sheets over the top. Distribute the spinach over the lasagne and then the ricotta. Spoon the tomatoes over the top and cover with foil. (The dish can be assembled to this stage ahead of time.) Turn the oven down to 180°C and bake for 20 minutes.

4. Remove the foil, sprinkle with the Parmesan and bake for another 15 minutes.

PER SERVE: 9 G FAT, 12 G DIETARY FIBRE, 1650 KJ (395 CALS)

 CUT INTO
6 PORTIONS
TO SERVE

RED PEPPER PASTA

Using evaporated skim milk is not the same as using cream, but it's a reasonable substitute.

1. Cook the pasta according to packet directions. Drain when cooked.
2. While the pasta is cooking, heat the oil in a large frying pan and cook the capsicum, onion and oregano over a gentle heat for about 5 minutes, covering with a lid to allow the onion to sweat. Stir several times.
3. Add the drained pasta and season generously with black pepper.
4. Beat the milk and eggs together and pour into the pasta mixture. Cook over a gentle heat, stirring constantly, until the mixture is thick. Serve sprinkled with the chives.

PER SERVE: 7 G FAT, 6 G DIETARY FIBRE, 1900 kJ (455 CALS)

375 g pasta shells,
   twists or bows
2 tsp olive oil
1 large red capsicum,
   seeded and sliced finely
1 medium onion,
   chopped finely
1 tsp dried oregano
freshly ground black pepper
1 cup evaporated skim milk
2 eggs
2 tbsp chopped chives

 SERVES 4

PENNE WITH GRILLED EGGPLANT AND ZUCCHINI

1 medium–large
   eggplant (about
   600 g) cut into 1.5
   cm slices
3 or 4 zucchini, sliced
400 g penne (or use
   pasta twists)
2 tbsp no-fat or low-
   Joule dressing
½ cup white wine
1 cup chopped
   fresh basil

1. Pre-heat the griller or barbecue and grill the eggplant and zucchini slices until soft and lightly brown on both sides. Cut into strips.
2. Cook the penne according to packet directions. Drain when cooked.
3. Heat the dressing and wine in a large frying pan. Add the grilled vegetables and basil and stir to combine. Serve on top of the penne.

PER SERVE: 2 G FAT, 8 G DIETARY FIBRE, 1640 kJ (390 CALS)

SERVES 4

SPAGHETTI WITH CHICKEN AND LEMON

A simple quick meal.

12 dried tomato halves

¾ cup boiling water

200 g spaghetti

2 tsp olive oil

1 small onion, sliced

1 clove garlic, crushed

1 skinless chicken breast
   fillet, about 150 g,
   sliced

2 tsp finely grated
   lemon rind

2 tbsp lemon juice

1 tbsp balsamic vinegar

2 tbsp chopped fresh basil

 SERVES 2

1. Place the tomatoes into a small bowl and cover with boiling water. Leave for 15 minutes.
2. Cook the spaghetti according to packet directions. Drain when cooked.
3. While the spaghetti is cooking, heat the olive oil in a frying pan, add the onion, garlic and chicken. stir-fry for 5 minutes, or until the chicken is brown but not dry. Add the lemon rind, juice, vinegar, basil and the tomatoes and their liquid and cook for 1 minute. Serve on drained spaghetti.

PER SERVE: 9 G FAT, 9 G DIETARY FIBRE, 2220 KJ (530 CALS)

UDON NOODLES WITH CHICKEN — SEE PAGE 44

SPAGHETTI WITH SMOKED SALMON — SEE PAGE 39

SPAGHETTI BOLOGNAISE

To make this suitable for gut-busters, use very lean mince (look for 95 per cent fat free on the label). Use a food processor to grate the vegetables.

1. Spray a heavy-based non-stick pan with the olive oil spray, add the mince, onion, garlic and basil and cook until the meat is brown.
2. Add the tomatoes, carrot, zucchini, mushrooms, tomato paste and wine and simmer for 30 minutes, stirring occasionally.
3. When the sauce has been simmering for about 15 minutes, cook the spaghetti according to packet directions. Drain when cooked and top with the Bolognaise sauce.

PER SERVE: 9 G FAT, 12 G DIETARY FIBRE, 2350 KJ (560 CALS)

olive oil spray
400 g ultra lean mince
1 large onion, chopped finely
2 cloves garlic, crushed
1 tsp dried basil
800 g can tomatoes,
*   no added salt, chopped*
1 large carrot, finely grated
2 zucchini, finely grated
250 g mushrooms, sliced
½ cup tomato paste
1 cup red wine
375 g spaghetti

 SERVES 4

SPAGHETTI WITH SMOKED SALMON

A simple dish that can be ready in less than 30 minutes.

6 medium tomatoes
400 g spaghetti
2 tsp olive oil
1 medium onion, cut
*   into wedges*
2 cloves garlic, crushed
1 cup fresh basil leaves
*   (or use chopped parsley)*
100 g smoked
*   salmon pieces*
½ cup (60 g) black olives

1. Heat a large saucepan of water for the spaghetti. Remove the cores from the tomatoes and then add the tomatoes to the boiling water. Leave the tomatoes in the water for 30 seconds, removing them with a slotted spoon. Allow them to cool a little, peel and dice.
2. Use the same water to cook the spaghetti according to packet directions.
3. While the spaghetti is cooking, heat the oil and gently cook the onion and garlic over a low heat for 4–5 minutes, stirring occasionally. Add the tomatoes, basil, salmon and olives and stir gently but do not boil.
4. Drain the spaghetti, place into individual bowls and top with the salmon and tomato. Serve with a green salad.

SERVES 4   **PER SERVE: 7 G FAT, 10 G DIETARY FIBRE, 1890 KJ (450 CALS)**

PENNE WITH TUNA

An easy meal to make using ingredients you probably have on hand. Serve with a salad or steamed beans, asparagus or broccoli.

20 dried tomato halves

250 g penne

2 tsp olive oil

1 medium onion,
    chopped finely

1 tsp dried mixed herbs

1 cup sliced mushrooms
    or celery

400 g can tuna in
    spring water or
    brine, drained

olive oil spray

200 g natural
    low-fat yoghurt

1 slice wholemeal bread

2 tbsp grated
    Parmesan cheese

2 tbsp chopped
    fresh parsley

1. Place the dried tomatoes in a small bowl and cover with boiling water. Leave to stand for 15 minutes, then drain and cut into smaller pieces. Keep the tomato water in the fridge and use it in place of stock.
2. Cook the penne according to packet directions. Drain when cooked.
3. While the penne is cooking, heat the oil in a frying pan and cook the onion and herbs over a gentle heat for 3–4 minutes. Add the mushrooms or celery and continue cooking for 2–3 minutes. Stir in the tuna and tomatoes.
4. Pre-heat the oven to 180°C and spray a casserole dish with olive oil.
5. Pour the yoghurt over the drained penne and stir to mix.
6. Place half the tuna mixture into a greased casserole dish, top with the penne and then the rest of the tuna mixture.
7. Using a food processor or blender, process the bread into crumbs. Combine the crumbs, cheese and parsley and sprinkle over the tuna. Bake for 15 minutes, or until the topping is golden.

PER SERVE: 8 G FAT, 6 G DIETARY FIBRE, 1880 KJ (450 CALS)

 SERVES 4

PRAWN AND ORANGE PASTA

A meal to make in 15 minutes and ideal for family or guests.

1. Cook the pasta according to packet directions. Drain when cooked.
2. While the pasta is cooking, steam the snow peas and asparagus for 2 minutes. Add the capsicum and prawns, and steam for a further 2 minutes.
3. Toss the vegetables and prawns with the hot pasta. Heat the orange juice and add to the pasta. Garnish with the orange segments and mint.

PER SERVE: 2 G FAT, 11 G DIETARY FIBRE, 1970 KJ (470 CALS)

375 g curly pasta

2 cups snow peas
    (topped and tailed)

1 bunch fresh asparagus
    cut into 3 cm lengths

1 red capsicum, seeded
    and cut into strips

12 green king prawns,
    peeled and de-veined

½ cup orange juice

2 oranges, peeled and cut
    into segments

1 tbsp chopped mint

 SERVES 4

EASY SUMMER PASTA

This no-fuss sauce leaves very little cleaning up, making it an appropriate meal on hot summer evenings.

200 g spaghetti

2 medium tomatoes

1 small red onion

finely grated peel and
    juice of one lemon

2 cups torn rocket leaves

½ cup torn basil or
    chopped mint

1. Cook the spaghetti according to packet directions. Drain.
2. While the spaghetti is cooking, dice the tomatoes and onion and combine with the lemon peel, juice and rocket. Serve on top of the hot pasta and sprinkle with the torn basil.

PER SERVE: 2 G FAT, 14 G DIETARY FIBRE, 2020 KJ (480 CALS)

 SERVES 2

FETTUCCINE WITH HAM, MUSHROOMS AND RED WINE

Quick and easy. The alcohol in the wine evaporates during cooking, so you can still feed this to the kids.

400 g fettuccine
2 tsp olive oil
1 large onion
 (preferably purple),
 sliced finely
2 cloves garlic, crushed
400 g mushrooms, sliced
1 cup red wine
2 tbsp tomato paste
100 g chopped lean ham

1. Cook the fettuccine according to packet directions. Drain when cooked.
2. While the fettuccine is cooking, heat the oil in a large heavy-based pan and gently cook the onion and garlic for 3–4 minutes. Add the mushrooms and cook for a few minutes until they begin to soften.
3. Add the wine and tomato paste, bring to the boil and cook for 3–4 minutes, stirring occasionally. Stir in the ham and serve on top of the fettuccine.

PER SERVE: 5 G FAT, 9 G DIETARY FIBRE, 1820 KJ (435 CALS)

 SERVES 4

PASTA WITH SPINACH AND RICOTTA

A creamy-tasting dish in spite of its low fat content. Use a smooth ricotta for the best texture.

1. Cook the pasta according to packet directions. Drain when cooked. If using a brand of fresh pasta that takes only 2–3 minutes to cook, prepare the sauce first.
2. Heat the spinach in the microwave or in a non-stick pan.
3. Combine the ricotta, garlic, lemon juice, mint and pepper and beat or blend until smooth. Stir in the spinach, adding about 1/2 cup of the cooking water from the pasta if necessary to make a smooth sauce. Pour the sauce over the hot drained pasta and toss to combine.

375 g fresh pasta
250 g frozen
 spinach, thawed
250 g fat-reduced
 smooth ricotta
1 clove garlic, crushed
¼ cup lemon juice
¼ cup fresh mint sprigs
freshly ground
 black pepper

PER SERVE: 7 G FAT, 7 G DIETARY FIBRE, 1570 KJ (375 CALS)

 SERVES 4

NOODLES WITH NUTS

This recipe uses rice noodles, but choose another variety if you prefer.

1. Toast the walnuts in a dry frying pan until brown. Set aside to cool.
2. Cook the noodles according to packet directions. Drain when cooked.
3. Heat a large frying pan or wok and add the oil, onion, garlic, chilli and broccoli. Put a lid over the pan and allow the vegetables to sweat for 4–5 minutes, stirring occasionally. Add the water chestnuts and heat through. Toss with the noodles, the lemon juice and basil and serve at once.

PER SERVE: 6 G FAT, 7 G DIETARY FIBRE, 1890 KJ (450 CALS)

2 tbsp walnut pieces

375 g flat rice noodles

2 tsp olive oil

1 medium onion, sliced

1 clove garlic, crushed

2 tsp finely chopped
  red chilli

500 g broccoli,
  broken into florets

170 g can water
  chestnuts, drained
  and sliced

2 tbsp lemon juice

½ cup torn basil leaves

 SERVES 4

UDON NOODLES WITH CHICKEN

Udon noodles are available in the refrigerator section of most supermarkets. They are made of wheat.

1 tsp sesame oil

150 g skinless
*   chicken breast*

1 tbsp Thai curry paste

1 medium carrot,
*   cut into thin strips*

100 g snow peas,
*   strings removed*

½ cup sliced
*   green shallots*

½ head Chinese cabbage

200 g fresh Udon noodles

2 tbsp lime juice

½ cup water

2 tsp fish sauce

2 cups mung
*   bean sprouts*

½ cup coriander leaves

 SERVES 2

1. Heat a wok or heavy-based frying pan, add the oil, chicken and curry paste and stir-fry for 2–3 minutes. Add the carrot and continue stir-frying for 2 minutes.
2. Add the snow peas, shallots, cabbage and noodles and stir-fry until the noodles are hot.
3. Add the lime juice, water and fish sauce and cook for a further minute.
4. Divide the mung beans into 2 deep bowls, pile the noodle mixture on top and sprinkle with coriander.

PER SERVE: 8 G FAT, 14 G DIETARY FIBRE, 2020 KJ (480 CALS)

SEAFOOD PAELLA

This impressive-looking dish is great for a dinner party. Use saffron threads rather than saffron powder, if possible, as the flavour is much better.

1. Heat the chicken stock and add the saffron. Leave to stand for 5 minutes.
2. Heat a large heavy-based frying pan (or use a paella pan, if available), add the oil and saute the onion, capsicum, garlic and chilli over a moderate heat until the onion softens. Add the rice, rosemary and pepper and stir well.
3. In a large steamer, heat the water and steam the mussels for 4–5 minutes, or until the shells open. Discard any that do not open. Strain the water and reserve.
4. Combine 1 cup of the reserved water from the mussels with the chicken stock and pour over the rice. Bring to the boil, turn the heat low, cover and simmer for 10 minutes.
5. Top the rice with the peas and prawns, cover and continue cooking for another 5 minutes or until the prawns turn pink. Decorate with the mussels and olives and sprinkle with the lemon juice and parsley. Serve straight from the pan.

PER SERVE: 7 G FAT, 7 G DIETARY FIBRE, 1800 KJ (430 CALS)

2 cups chicken stock
1 tsp saffron threads
1 tbsp olive oil
1 large onion, sliced
1 red capsicum, seeded and sliced into strips
2 cloves garlic, crushed
1 tsp finely chopped chilli
250 g long grain rice
2 tbsp chopped fresh rosemary
½ tsp coarsely ground black pepper
1 cup water
16 mussels, scrubbed
250 g frozen peas
16 green prawns (leave shells and heads on)
8 black or green olives
2 tbsp lemon juice
2 tbsp finely chopped parsley

 SERVES 4

VEGETABLE PILAF

Serve with a simple green salad or as an accompaniment to barbecued fish.

1 tbsp olive oil
2 large leeks, washed
and sliced
2 cloves garlic
300 g mushrooms,
sliced
2 cups long grain rice
6 cardamom pods
3 ½ cups chicken stock
½ cup white wine
1 bunch asparagus or
250 g green beans,
cut into 3 cm lengths

 SERVES 4

1. In a large pan with a tight-fitting lid, heat the oil and cook the leeks, garlic and mushrooms over a moderate heat for 2–3 minutes.
2. Add the rice and cardamom pods and stir well to coat the rice with oil. Stir in the chicken stock and wine, bring to the boil, cover and simmer for 15 minutes.
3. Add the asparagus or beans and continue cooking, covered, for another 5 minutes. Remove the cardamom pods before serving.

PER SERVE: 6 G FAT, 7 G DIETARY FIBRE, 1930 KJ (460 CALS)

SALMON AND RICE CAKE

A simple, quick dish that only needs a green salad for accompaniment.

1. Place the rice, water and thyme in a saucepan, bring to the boil, cover and simmer over a low heat for 30 minutes, or until all the water is absorbed. Alternatively, use 3 cups of cooked boiled rice.
2. Preheat the oven to 180°C and spray a 20 cm cake tin with olive oil spray.
3. Combine the rice, salmon, capsicum, shallots and peas and spoon into the cake tin, smoothing the top. Beat the eggs and yoghurt together and pour over the rice. Sprinkle with the paprika and bake for 20 minutes.

PER SERVE: 8 G FAT, 6 G DIETARY FIBRE, 1710 KJ (410 CALS)

1 cup brown rice
2 cups water
1 tsp dried thyme leaves
olive oil spray
400 g can red skinless salmon, drained and flaked
1 red capsicum, seeded and diced
1 cup sliced green shallots
250 g frozen peas, thawed
2 eggs, beaten
400 g low-fat natural yoghurt
1 tsp paprika

 SERVES 4

Pumpkin, capsicum and mushroom risotto

Arborio rice is now available in supermarkets. It absorbs much more water than other rice without going soggy. This dish won't be successful with regular rice.

about 500 g pumpkin,
   cut into 2.5 cm cubes
olive oil spray
1 tbsp olive oil
1 medium onion,
   chopped finely
1 red capsicum, seeded
   and sliced
1 tsp dried rosemary
400 g (2 cups)
   Arborio rice
½ cup white wine
5 cups hot chicken stock
1 cup frozen peas, thawed
½ cup chopped parsley
2 tbsp grated
   Parmesan cheese

1. Preheat the oven to 180°C. Place the pumpkin cubes on a shallow oven dish and spray lightly with olive oil spray. Roast for 15 minutes.
2. Heat the oil in a saucepan and gently cook the onion, capsicum and rosemary for 2–3 minutes. Add the rice and stir until it is coated with oil.
3. Add the wine and about 1/2 cup of hot the stock to the rice and cook, stirring occasionally, until the liquid is absorbed. Continue adding the hot stock, about 1 cup at a time, allowing the rice to absorb each cup before adding the next. Stir occasionally. It will take about 25 minutes for all the stock to be absorbed.
4. When adding the last of the stock, also add the peas and roasted pumpkin and stir gently to combine. When the stock has been absorbed, add the parsley and stir to combine. Put a lid on the saucepan, turn off the heat and leave to stand for 3–4 minutes. Serve topped with the Parmesan cheese.

Per serve: 8 g fat, 8 g dietary fibre, 2040 kJ (490 Cals)

 Serves 4

CHICKEN AND RICE BAKE

A good way to use leftover rice and chicken. Serve with a green salad.

1. Preheat the oven to 180°C. Spray a casserole dish (or 4 large individual ovenproof dishes) with olive oil spray.
2. Combine the rice, chicken, corn, shallots, celery, mushrooms, capsicums and mint and spoon into the prepared dishes.
3. Beat the eggs and milk together and pour over the rice mixture. Sprinkle with the cheese and bake for 30–40 minutes. If using individual dishes, turn them out to serve.

PER SERVE: 6 G FAT, 5 G DIETARY FIBRE, 1750 KJ (420 CALS)

olive oil spray

3 cups cooked rice

1 cup cooked diced chicken (or turkey)

400 g can corn kernels, drained

½ cup sliced green shallots

½ cup sliced celery

1 cup sliced mushrooms

½ red capsicum, seeded and diced

½ green capsicum, seeded and diced

2 tbsp chopped mint

2 eggs

1 cup evaporated skim milk

1 tbsp grated Parmesan cheese

 SERVES 4

MUSHROOM AND SWEET POTATO RICE PIE

A great alternative to high-fat pastry. Use leftover brown rice or cook ¾ cup raw brown rice in 1½ cups of water or stock and cool slightly.

Crust

olive oil spray

2 cups cooked brown rice

2 tbsp sunflower seeds

1 egg, beaten

Filling

2 tsp olive oil

1 small onion,
   chopped finely

1 stalk celery, sliced finely

200 g mushrooms, sliced

2 cups cooked
   sliced broccoli

2 cups orange sweet
   potato, sliced thinly

60 g (½ cup) grated
   reduced-fat cheddar
   (7 per cent fat)

12 black olives

1. Preheat the oven to 180°C and spray a 20 cm pie dish with olive oil spray.
2. Combine the rice, sunflower seeds and egg and mix thoroughly. Press the mixture into the prepared dish to form a pie shell and bake for 20 minutes.
3. While the pie shell is cooking, heat the oil and cook the onion, celery and mushrooms for 2–3 minutes. Tip the onion mixture into the cooked pie shell and top with the broccoli. Cook the sweet potato in the frying pan for about 3 minutes, turning once. Place the sweet potato on top of broccoli and press down with an egg slice. Sprinkle with the cheese, dot the top with the olives and bake for 15 minutes, or until the cheese is melted and brown. Cut into wedges to serve.

PER SERVE: 8 G FAT, 8 G DIETARY FIBRE, 1290 KJ (310 CALS)

 SERVES 4

POLENTA WITH RATATOUILLE SAUCE

Instant polenta is as nutritious as the regular variety and cooks in just 3 minutes instead of 25. Make the polenta ahead for best results.

1. Place the boiling water in a saucepan and add the polenta in a steady stream, stirring constantly. Cook for 3 minutes, stirring and taking care that the spitting polenta does not burn you. Add the salt. Pour the cooked polenta into a non-stick cake tin and leave it to cool. Refrigerate until required.
2. Heat the oil in a large frying pan and cook the onion over a moderate heat, without browning, for 3–4 minutes. Add the oregano, eggplant, capsicum and zucchini and continue cooking, stirring occasionally for about 10 minutes. Add the tomatoes, cover and cook for a further 10 minutes.
3. Cut the polenta into triangles and grill until browned on both sides. Serve with the ratatouille sauce.

PER SERVE: 8 G FAT, 12 G DIETARY FIBRE, 1680 KJ (400 CALS)

3 cups boiling water
1 cup instant polenta
pinch salt
2 tsp olive oil
1 onion, sliced
1 tsp dried oregano leaves
1 small eggplant, about 300 g, diced
1 capsicum, seeded and diced
2 zucchini, cut into chunks
400 g canned tomatoes, no added salt, chopped roughly

 SERVES 2

BARLEY PILAF

This pilaf is delicious with grilled lamb or served simply with a tossed salad. Wholegrain barley is available in the health food section of most supermarkets.

2 tbsp slivered almonds

2 tsp olive oil

1 medium onion,
    chopped

250 g (1½ cups)
    wholegrain barley

3 cups vegetable or
    chicken stock

½ cup orange juice

¼ cup currants

½ cup chopped
    dried apricots

10 cm piece
    cinnamon stick

6 cardamom pods

 SERVES 4

1. Toast the almonds in a dry frying pan until golden brown. Set aside.
2. Heat the oil in a saucepan and gently cook the onion until lightly browned. Add the barley and stir for 2–3 minutes.
3. Add the stock, juice, currants, apricots, cinnamon and cardamom. Bring to the boil, cover tightly and simmer for 50 minutes or until the liquid is absorbed and the barley is tender. Remove the cinnamon and cardamom pods and stir in the toasted almonds. Serve at once.

PER SERVE: 7 G FAT, 10 G DIETARY FIBRE, 1150 KJ (275 CALS)

SPICY BUCKWHEAT

Delicious with roast lamb or chicken.

1 Toast the peanuts in a dry frying pan until brown. Set aside to cool.
2. Heat the oil in a saucepan and cook the onion and garlic over moderate heat for 2–3 minutes. Add the buckwheat groats, coriander, cumin and chilli and stir for 3–4 minutes.
3. Add the stock (or water) and raisins and bring to the boil, cover and simmer for 15 minutes.
4. Serve topped with the roasted peanuts and chopped coriander.

PER SERVE: 8 G FAT, 4 G DIETARY FIBRE, 1280 KJ (305 CALS)

¼ cup unsalted peanuts

2 tsp olive oil

1 medium onion, sliced

1 clove garlic, crushed

1 cup buckwheat groats

1 tbsp ground coriander

2 tsp ground cumin

1 tsp chopped chilli

2 cups stock, or water

½ cup raisins

2 tbsp chopped
    coriander

 SERVES 4

COUSCOUS WITH ROASTED ROSEMARY VEGETABLES

If you're pressed for time, you can place the couscous in a bowl and pour boiling water over it, but it's much lighter and better if you steam it. Harissa will be much too hot for most children, so serve it separately.

1 cup couscous
1 orange sweet potato, about 350 g
1 small butternut pumpkin
1 red capsicum
1 yellow capsicum
1 green capsicum
1 head garlic
olive oil spray
fresh rosemary
2 tsp extra virgin olive oil
2 tbsp preserved lemon, chopped finely
1 cup chicken or vegetable stock
1 tsp harissa paste

 SERVES 4

1. Preheat the oven to 180°C.
2. Place the couscous in a fine sieve and run under the cold tap until it is thoroughly wet. Tip into a large bowl and leave for 5 minutes, breaking up any lumps with your fingers. Sprinkle with ½ cup cold water and work gently with your fingers until the water is absorbed. Place the couscous in the top section of a steamer and steam, uncovered, for 10 minutes.
3. While the couscous is steaming, peel the sweet potato and pumpkin and cut into 2.5 cm cubes. Remove the seeds from the capsicums and cut each one into about 8 pieces. Cut through the whole garlic head and place cut side up with the other vegetables on an oven tray. Spray all the vegetables with olive oil spray, cover with the fresh rosemary sprigs and bake for 30 minutes, turning the vegetables once.
4. Tip the couscous into a bowl and sprinkle with the olive oil. Leave to stand for 10 minutes, then re-steam it in the top section of a steamer for 10–15 minutes.
5. When the vegetables are cooked, remove the rosemary and squeeze the garlic from the cloves, discarding the garlic skin. Mound the couscous onto a large serving plate and top with the vegetables and preserved lemon.
6. Heat the stock, stir in the harissa and serve separately to be poured over vegetables and couscous.

PER SERVE: 5 G FAT, 9 G DIETARY FIBRE, 1060 KJ (255 CALS)

COUSCOUS WITH ROASTED ROSEMARY VEGETABLES — SEE PAGE 54

SEAFOOD PAELLA — SEE PAGE 45

COUSCOUS WITH SPICED CHICK PEAS AND PUMPKIN

This recipe uses the quick method to prepare the couscous. However, if desired, steam the couscous as in the previous recipe for a lighter result.

1. In a plastic bag combine the cinnamon, cumin, coriander, brown sugar and chilli. Add the mint and pumpkin and shake well to coat the pumpkin with the flavourings.
2. Preheat the oven to 180°C. Spray an oven tray with olive oil spray and add the pumpkin and spices. Roast for 15 minutes, turning the pieces once. Add the chick peas, tossing to combine, and continue cooking for 5–10 minutes or until the pumpkin is tender.
3. To prepare the couscous by the quick method, place it into a bowl. Heat the stock to boiling point and pour over the couscous. Cover with foil and leave to stand for about 10 minutes, when the couscous will have absorbed the liquid.
4. When the vegetables are done, add the lemon juice to the couscous and serve topped with the pumpkin and chick peas and the fresh coriander.

2 tsp cinnamon
2 tsp cumin
1 tbsp ground coriander
2 tsp brown sugar
1 tsp dried chilli
2 tbsp chopped mint
6 cups pumpkin cubes
olive oil spray
400 g can chick
    peas, drained
1 cup couscous
2 cups chicken or
    vegetable stock
2 tbsp lemon juice
½ cup fresh
    coriander sprigs

PER SERVE: 4 G FAT, 7 G DIETARY FIBRE, 1040 KJ (250 CALS)

 SERVES 4

SOUPS

When you're hungry, home-made soups are a great idea. They're delicious and filling—and our recipes are ideal because they have few kilojoules. Steaming hot hearty soups are great in winter, but don't forget you can also enjoy chilled soups in summer. Soups are great for lunch, and you can use them either as a first course or a complete meal at dinner. A bowl of soup is also a satisfying snack between meals. Try taking soups to work—in a thermos flask if you're on the road or to reheat in a microwave, where that's appropriate.

TIPS

Coconut milk is high in fat (14–36 per cent fat, depending on the brand), so make sure you use a light variety (5 per cent fat). Tip whatever is left in the can into a freezer container and keep for next time.

Regular cheddar cheese has 33 per cent fat. Most reduced-fat cheddar cheese has 25 per cent fat, but it's worth checking the label because one of the best-tasting reduced-fat cheeses has only 7 per cent fat.

A heavy-based non-stick pan reduces the oil needed when cooking onions. Cover with a lid to sweat so the onions don't burn.

Pappadams have no fat but soak up plenty if they are fried in oil. For an easy no-fat alternative, cook pappadams singly in the microwave for 20–40 seconds each or until they puff. Be careful, however, as they can burn easily.

LAKSA

This is a hearty meal-in-one dish with loads of flavour.

1. Shell and de-vein the prawns, leaving the tails on, and put aside. To make the stock, place the shells in a saucepan, add the water, bring to the boil, cover and simmer for 10 minutes. Strain the stock into a bowl and discard the shells.
2. Place the noodles in a large bowl and cover with boiling water. Leave for 5 minutes, then drain and keep hot.
3. In a large wok heat the sesame oil and cook the onion, garlic, lemon grass and lime leaves (both optional) over a medium heat for 3–4 minutes. Add the laksa paste and cook for another minute.
4. Add the strained prawn stock, cabbage or other greens, beans and capsicum, bring to the boil and cook for 2 minutes. Add the prawns and cook for 1–2 minutes, or until they turn pink. Stir in the coconut milk.
5. Divide the bean sprouts between 4 large bowls. Top with the noodles and then ladle the hot soup over the top. Garnish with the coriander.

Variation: in place of prawns, use 300 g tofu or 400 g boneless fish cut into 2 cm cubes.

PER SERVE: 7 G FAT, 8 G DIETARY FIBRE, 1325 KJ (315 CALS)

20 green prawns
  (medium or king)
6 cups water
200 g fresh noodles
2 tsp sesame oil
1 large onion, sliced
2 cloves garlic, crushed
1 tbsp finely sliced
  lemon grass (white
  part only), optional
3 kaffir lime leaves,
  shredded finely,
  optional
2 tbsp laksa paste
2 cups sliced Chinese
  cabbage or
  Asian greens
200 g green beans,
  trimmed and cut
  into 5 cm lengths
1 red capsicum, seeded
  and sliced
1 cup light
  coconut milk
250 g fresh mung
  bean sprouts
½ cup chopped
  fresh coriander

 SERVES 4

SPICY THAI FISH SOUP

A great soup to serve when you want lots of flavour.

1 tsp sesame oil

1 tbsp lemon grass
    (white part only),
    sliced finely

2 tsp finely
    chopped ginger

1–2 tsp chopped chilli

1 tbsp red curry paste

6 cups water

500 g boneless fish
    fillets, cut into
    2.5 cm cubes

1 cup sliced
    green shallots

1 red capsicum,
    seeded and sliced

150 g button
    mushrooms, sliced

2 tbsp lime juice

1 tbsp fish sauce

½ cup fresh
    coriander leaves

½ cup Vietnamese
    mint leaves

1. In a large saucepan or wok heat the sesame oil and add the lemon grass, ginger, chilli and curry paste. stir-fry over a moderate heat for 1–2 minutes.
2. Add the water, fish, shallots, capsicum and mushrooms, bring to the boil and cook for 3–4 minutes, or until the fish is white and flakes easily with a fork. (Do not overcook or the fish will toughen.) Stir in the lime juice and the fish sauce and serve at once in large bowls. Sprinkle the coriander and mint on top.

Variation: substitute 400 g sliced chicken breast for the fish.

PER SERVE: 3 G FAT, 2 G DIETARY FIBRE, 800 KJ (190 CALS)

 SERVES 4

POTATO SOUP

An excellent low-fat but creamy-tasting, filling, comforting soup for cold winter days.

1. Place the stock, potatoes, leek, bay leaves and mint in a large saucepan. Bring to the boil, cover and simmer for 15–20 minutes, or until the potatoes are tender. Remove the bay leaves and mint.
2. Puree the soup in batches in a blender, adding the skim milk powder and nutmeg. Return to a saucepan and reheat gently, stirring constantly (take care, as the soup may splutter). Serve in deep bowls garnished with the dill or parsley.

PER SERVE: 1 G FAT, 4 G DIETARY FIBRE, 940 KJ (225 CALS)

1 L chicken stock
800 g potatoes, peeled and
    cut into large chunks
1 medium leek (white part
    only), washed and sliced
3 bay leaves
some mint sprigs
¾ cup skim milk powder
pinch nutmeg
1 tbsp chopped dill
    or parsley

 SERVES 4

FRENCH ONION SOUP

Always delicious, but usually high in fat. Use a reduced-fat cheddar with 7 per cent fat.

1 tbsp olive oil
1 kg onions, sliced thinly
1 tsp dried thyme
2 tsp sugar
5 cups beef stock
1 tbsp balsamic vinegar
4 bay leaves
4 slices French bread
2 tbsp Dijon-style mustard
60 g (½ cup) grated
    reduced-fat cheddar
    (7 per cent fat)

1. Place the oil, onions and thyme in a large heavy-based pot and cook over a very low heat, stirring occasionally, for 30 minutes.
2. Add the sugar, stock, vinegar and bay leaves, bring to the boil, then cover and simmer for 10 minutes.
3. Preheat the oven to 180°C. Spread the bread with the mustard, place on a baking tray and bake for 5–10 minutes, or until the bread is crisp.
4. Sprinkle the cheese over the bread slices and place into 4 serving bowls. Ladle the soup over the bread and serve at once.

PER SERVE: 7 G FAT, 5 G DIETARY FIBRE, 975 KJ (230 CALS)

SERVES 4

ROASTED PUMPKIN SOUP

Roasting pumpkin brings out its flavour. It's also easier to remove the skin from most pumpkins after roasting.

1.5 kg pumpkin, cut
    into chunks, seeds
    removed
1 large onion, peeled
    and halved
3 large cloves garlic
olive oil spray
1 tsp dried thyme
piece of orange peel,
    about 10 cm long
4 cups chicken stock
pinch nutmeg
½ cup low-fat
    natural yoghurt
2 tsp finely grated
    orange peel
black pepper

1. Pre-heat the oven to 180°C. Place the pumpkin, onion and unpeeled garlic on a baking dish and spray with olive oil so that the oil forms a thin film on the vegetables. (Alternatively, heat 1 tsp olive oil in the baking tray and roll the vegetables in it.) Bake for about 45 minutes or until the pumpkin flesh is tender. When cool enough to handle, peel the pumpkin and discard the skin.
2. In a large saucepan combine the pumpkin flesh, onion, the flesh squeezed from the garlic plus the thyme, orange peel and stock. Bring to the boil, cover and simmer for 5 minutes.
3. Remove the orange rind and puree the soup in batches in a food processor or blender, adding the nutmeg. Return the soup to a saucepan and reheat. Serve topped with a dollop of yoghurt, the finely grated orange rind and a sprinkling of pepper.

PER SERVE: 3 G FAT, 4 G DIETARY FIBRE, 665 KJ (160 CALS)

 SERVES 4

ORANGE SWEET POTATO SOUP

A deliciously easy soup with a natural sweetness.

1. Heat the oil in a large saucepan and cook the onion over a gentle heat for 3–4 minutes.
2. Add the sweet potato and herbs and cook for a further 2–3 minutes, stirring to coat the sweet potato with any oil remaining.
3. Pour in the stock or water and the orange juice, bring to the boil, cover and simmer for 12–15 minutes, or until the sweet potato is soft.
4. Puree the soup in batches until smooth. Return to the saucepan and reheat, stirring constantly. Ladle the soup into serving bowls and top each with a dollop of yoghurt and a sprinkle of parsley and pepper. Draw a fork or skewer through the yoghurt to make an attractive pattern.

2 tsp olive oil
1 medium onion, chopped
1 kg sweet potatoes, peeled and cut into large chunks
2 tsp dried mixed herbs
4 cups chicken stock or water
½ cup orange juice
½ cup low-fat natural yoghurt
1 tbsp chopped fresh parsley
freshly ground black pepper

PER SERVE: 3 G FAT, 5 G DIETARY FIBRE, 1025 KJ (245 CALS)

SERVES 4

FRESH MUSHROOM SOUP

This soup is extra good, if you can find or buy field mushrooms with their rich earthy flavour.

2 tsp olive oil
1 medium onion, chopped
1 clove garlic, crushed
500 g mushrooms (preferably dark field mushrooms), sliced
1 tsp dried oregano
3 bay leaves
4 cups water
2 tbsp brandy
1 cup fat-reduced evaporated milk
2 tbsp chopped chives

1. In a large saucepan heat the oil and cook the onion and garlic for 3–4 minutes over a gentle heat until soft. Add the mushrooms and oregano and stir to combine. Add the bay leaves and water, bring to the boil, cover and simmer for about 10 minutes. Remove the bay leaves.
2. Puree the soup in a blender, adding the brandy and evaporated milk. Return to a saucepan and reheat, stirring constantly. Serve sprinkled with chives.

PER SERVE: 4 G FAT, 4 G DIETARY FIBRE, 600 KJ (145 CALS)

SERVES 4

CURRIED CAULIFLOWER SOUP

An Indian-inspired soup that is excellent served with pappadams.

1 tbsp ground coriander

1 tsp ground cumin

1 tsp ground turmeric

2 tsp mustard seeds

2 tsp mustard seed oil
   (or macadamia nut oil)

1 medium onion,
   chopped finely

2 cloves garlic, crushed

1–2 tsp chopped chilli

2 tsp finely
   chopped ginger

1 small cauliflower,
broken into florets
   and sliced

4 cups water

2 tbsp lemon juice

1. Heat a heavy-based saucepan over a moderate heat. Add the coriander, cumin, turmeric and mustard seeds and stir for 1–2 minutes, or until the mustard seeds begin to pop and the spices are toasted but not burnt.

2. Add the oil, onion, garlic, chilli and ginger and stir-fry over a gentle heat for 3–4 minutes, or until the onion begins to soften. Do not allow the onion to burn.

3. Add the cauliflower and water, bring to the boil, cover and simmer for 10 minutes, or until the cauliflower is just tender. Add the lemon juice and serve.

PER SERVE: 3 G FAT, 4 G DIETARY FIBRE, 330 KJ (80 CALS)

 SERVES 4

HOME-MADE TOMATO SOUP

Make this soup in late summer when tomatoes are at their best and are usually cheap. Straining the tomatoes might seem like a lot of bother, but little bits of skin left behind if you don't, make the soup unpleasant.

1. In a large saucepan, heat the oil and add the onion and garlic. Cover and allow to sweat over a low–moderate heat, stirring occasionally, for 5 minutes.
2. Add the tomatoes, tomato paste, water, wine, mint and sugar. Bring to the boil, cover and simmer for 5 minutes. Remove the mint.
3. Puree the soup in a blender until smooth, then push through a strainer to remove any bits of skin. Reheat and serve at once, or alternatively chill until required. To serve, garnish each bowl with pepper and chopped mint. Add a swirl of low-fat natural yoghurt if desired.

PER SERVE: 3 G FAT, 5 G DIETARY FIBRE, 350 KJ (85 CALS)

2 tsp olive oil
2 medium onions,
chopped roughly
2 cloves garlic, crushed
1 kg tomatoes,
chopped roughly
2 tbsp tomato paste
4 cups water
½ cup red wine
2–3 sprigs fresh mint
1 tsp sugar
freshly ground pepper
1 tbsp chopped mint
¼ cup low-fat
natural yoghurt
(optional)

 SERVES 4

CABBAGE AND POTATO SOUP

This hearty soup is filling and excellent on cold days.

4 slices French bread

1 clove garlic, peeled
　and cut in half

2 tsp olive oil

1 medium onion,
　chopped finely

1 clove garlic, crushed

1 tsp dried thyme

500 g small
　potatoes, halved

3 cups chicken stock

400 g can tomatoes,
　no added salt

2 medium
　zucchini, sliced

4 cups shredded
　green cabbage

1 red capsicum, seeded
　and sliced

 SERVES 4

1. Preheat the oven to 180°C. Rub the bread with the cut clove of garlic and bake the bread directly on the oven shelf for 10–15 minutes, or until crisp.
2. Heat the oil in a large saucepan, add the onion, garlic and thyme, cover and sweat for 3–4 minutes.
3. Add the potatoes, stock and tomatoes, bring to the boil, cover and simmer for 10 minutes. Add the zucchini, cabbage and capsicum and simmer for a further 3–4 minutes.
4. Place a slice of the oven-toasted bread into each bowl and ladle the soup over the top. Serve at once.

PER SERVE: 4 G FAT, 9 G DIETARY FIBRE, 1030 KJ (245 CALS)

PEASANT SOUP

Make a big pot of this delicious soup for a meal or just a snack. One serving provides half your daily fibre needs. It also freezes well.

1. Place the chicken stock in a large saucepan, add the lentils, bring to the boil, cover and simmer for 10 minutes.
2. Add the vegetables and simmer for a further 10–15 minutes, or until the vegetables are tender.
3. Add the chick peas and their liquid and heat through. Serve topped with parsley and pepper.

PER SERVE: 3 G FAT, 15 G DIETARY FIBRE, 1280 KJ (305 CALS)

8 cups chicken stock
1 cup red lentils
10 cups chopped vegetables (choose from broccoli, cauliflower, onion, potato, pumpkin, zucchini, cabbage, carrot, parsnip, squash, mushrooms, spinach, peas, green beans)
420 g can chick peas
½ cup chopped parsley
freshly ground black pepper

 SERVES 4

CHICKEN AND CORN SOUP

A delicious Asian-style soup.

4 cups chicken stock
400 g chicken breast fillet, cut into strips
440 g can corn kernels
1 cup sliced green shallots
1 small red chilli, seeded and chopped
1 egg
2 egg whites
1 tbsp lime or lemon juice
1 tsp sesame oil
fresh coriander leaves

1. In a large saucepan, heat the chicken stock to boiling point. Add the chicken strips and simmer for 3–4 minutes. Add the undrained corn kernels, shallots and chilli.
2. Beat the egg and the egg whites until well combined, then dribble slowly into the hot soup, stirring continuously. Add the lime or lemon juice and sesame oil and serve immediately. Garnish each bowl with coriander.

PER SERVE: 6 G FAT, 3 G DIETARY FIBRE, 1025 KJ (245 CALS)

SERVES 4

MINESTRONE

A fast and easy-to-prepare version of an old classic. Add some crusty bread and make a meal of it.

6 cups chicken stock

1 large onion,
   chopped finely

1 stick celery, sliced

2 medium carrots,
   sliced finely

1 leek, washed and sliced

800 g can tomatoes,
   chopped roughly

2 tbsp tomato paste

1 tsp dried basil

4 bay leaves

100 g small pasta shells

440 g can red
   kidney beans

440 g can chick peas

2 cups shredded cabbage

2 cups shredded
   English spinach

100 g mushrooms, sliced

2 tbsp torn basil leaves

2 tbsp finely grated
   Parmesan cheese

 SERVES 6

1. In a large saucepan place the stock, onion, celery, carrots, leek, tomatoes, tomato paste, basil and bay leaves. Bring to the boil, add the pasta and simmer for 5 minutes. Remove the bay leaves.
2. Add the undrained beans, chick peas, cabbage, spinach and mushrooms and simmer for a further 5 minutes. Ladle into bowls and sprinkle with the basil and cheese.

PER SERVE: 4 G FAT, 12 G DIETARY FIBRE, 990 KJ (235 CALS)

SPLIT PEA AND BACON SOUP

Ask the butcher or delicatessen for lean bacon bones.

1. Place bacon bones, water, split peas, onion, celery, bay leaves and thyme in a large saucepan. Bring to the boil, cover and simmer for 45 minutes or until the peas are tender. Remove the bay leaves and bacon bones.
2. Add the potatoes and cook for a further 10 minutes, then add the peas and cook until they defrost and are heated through. Ladle the soup into bowls and sprinkle each serving with lemon juice and parsley.

PER SERVE: 2 G FAT, 14 G DIETARY FIBRE, 1500 KJ (360 CALS)

250 g bacon bones,
   trimmed of all fat

8 cups water

375 g (2 cups) green
   split peas

1 medium onion,
   chopped finely

1 stick celery,
   sliced finely

3 bay leaves

1 tsp dried thyme leaves

2 medium
   potatoes, diced

1 cup frozen peas

1 tbsp lemon juice

2 tbsp finely chopped
   flat leaf parsley

 SERVES 4

LAMB SHANK AND LENTIL SOUP

This is a meal-in-a-pot. It takes a while to cook, but it can be made ahead and frozen until needed.

2 lamb shanks,
   trimmed of fat
1 large onion, chopped
2 tsp mixed dried herbs
4 bay leaves
6 cups water
1 cup red wine
   (or use extra water)
1 cup brown lentils
½ cup brown rice
2 carrots, sliced
250 g mushrooms,
   preferably field
   mushrooms, sliced
4 medium
   zucchini, sliced
250 g frozen peas

1. Heat a large flameproof non-stick casserole or saucepan and brown the shanks on all sides. Add the onion and herbs, cover and allow to sweat for 4–5 minutes, stirring occasionally.
2. Add the bay leaves, water, wine and lentils, bring to the boil, cover and simmer for 1½ hours.
3. Stir in the rice, carrots and mushrooms, cover and continue cooking for another 20 minutes.
4. Remove the shanks and separate the meat from the bones. Discard the bones. Add the meat, zucchini and peas to the soup and simmer for a further 5 minutes.

PER SERVE: 4 G FAT, 14 G DIETARY FIBRE, 1430 KJ (340 CALS)

 SERVES 4

LAKSA — SEE PAGE 59

MINESTRONE — SEE PAGE 68

SEAFOOD SOUP

This soup is a complete meal, ideal for a special occasion. Ask your fishmonger for bones to make the fish stock. If unavailable, use water.

1. Place the fish trimmings, prawn shells (if used), water, carrot, wine, parsley, tarragon and lemon peel in a large saucepan. Bring to the boil, cover and simmer for 20 minutes. Strain the fish stock and set aside.
2. Heat the oil and gently saute the onion and garlic until softened, but not brown.
3. Add the potatoes, leek and fish stock (or water), bring to the boil, cover and simmer for 20 minutes. Puree in a blender or food processor. Return to a saucepan and reheat.
4. Add the fish and simmer for 3 minutes. Then add the scallops and prawns and cook for 2 minutes or until the prawns are pink. Serve at once, in large bowls, garnished with dill or parsley and a lemon wedge.

PER SERVE: 4 G FAT, 4 G DIETARY FIBRE, 1190 KJ (285 CALS)

For fish stock
*approximately 750 g fish
    bones, trimmings or
    fish head*
shells from prawns, if using
1.5 L cold water
1 carrot, sliced
1 cup white wine
few sprigs parsley
*few sprigs tarragon or ½ tsp
    dried tarragon leaves*
piece of lemon peel

For soup
2 tsp olive oil
1 medium onion, sliced
2 cloves garlic, crushed
*500 g potatoes, peeled
    and sliced*
1 leek, cleaned and sliced
500 g boneless fish fillets
12 scallops
*12 green king
    prawns, peeled*
*freshly snipped dill or
    chopped parsley*
4 lemon wedges

 SERVES 4

BEAN SOUP

A quick and easy way to get lots of fibre and flavour in the same bowl.

2 tsp olive oil
1 onion, diced
2 cloves garlic, crushed
1 tsp ground cumin
1 tbsp ground coriander
415 g can soy beans
  in tomato sauce
420 g can chick peas,
  preferably spicy
  Moroccan variety
400 g can tomatoes in
  tomato juice, no
  added salt
finely chopped fresh mint

 SERVES 4

1. Place the oil, onion and garlic in a large saucepan. Cover and allow to sweat for about 5 minutes, stirring occasionally. Add the cumin and coriander and stir for 1 minute.
2. Add the undrained soy beans, chick peas and tomatoes and heat to boiling. Serve in deep bowls, sprinkled with mint.

PER SERVE: 8 G FAT, 18 G DIETARY FIBRE, 1275 KJ (305 CALS)

SPINACH AND BUTTERMILK SOUP

This soup is a great way to use spinach or silver beet from your garden. You can also use frozen spinach—a convenient and nutritious product.

1. Place the rice and vegetable stock in a large saucepan, bring to the boil and simmer for 15 minutes.
2. Add the spinach and continue cooking until the spinach is defrosted (or wilted, if using fresh spinach). Add the coriander and mint and turn off the heat. Allow to cool a little.
3. Puree the soup in batches and stir in the buttermilk. Chill for at least an hour. Just before serving, stir in the lemon juice.

PER SERVE: 5 G FAT, 5 G DIETARY FIBRE, 905 KJ (215 CALS)

½ cup brown rice
1 L vegetable stock
500 g fresh or frozen
   spinach
½ cup chopped fresh
   coriander leaves
½ cup chopped
   fresh mint
600 mL fat-reduced
   buttermilk
1 tbsp lemon juice

 SERVES 4

BEETROOT SOUP

This recipe is easy to make, especially with a food processor. Serve it chilled on a hot day. It is low in fat and kilojoules and high in dietary fibre.

1 tbsp olive oil

1 medium onion,
   chopped

4 beetroot, peeled and
   grated (or use 800 g
   can of whole
   beetroot, including
   liquid)

1 large apple, peeled,
   cored and sliced

1 cup shredded
   red cabbage

1 L chicken stock

2 tbsp tomato puree
   (no added salt)

½ cup red wine

3 bay leaves

2 tbsp lemon juice

freshly ground pepper

200 g low-fat natural
   yoghurt for garnish

2 tbsp chopped parsley

1. Heat the oil in a large saucepan and cook the onion for 2–3 minutes over a gentle heat until softened but not brown.
2. Add the beetroot, apple, cabbage, stock, tomato puree, red wine and bay leaves, bring to the boil, cover and simmer for 20 minutes. Remove the bay leaves. Just before serving, add the lemon juice and freshly ground pepper. Serve hot or cool (chill until required). Top each serve with a dollop of yoghurt and swirl with a fork to produce a striped effect. Sprinkle with parsley.

PER SERVE: 6 G FAT, 7 G DIETARY FIBRE, 765 KJ (180 CALS)

 SERVES 4

FRUIT SOUP

Serve as a soup, a dessert or even for breakfast or brunch.

1. Place the apple juice, water, apricots, apples, sultanas, cinnamon stick, cloves and rice or sago into a large saucepan or basin, cover and leave to soak for at least an hour, or leave in the refrigerator overnight.
2. Bring the mixture to the boil, cover and simmer gently for 15 minutes. Remove the cinnamon stick and cloves. Serve hot or cool (chill until required). This is delicious with a dollop of low-fat yoghurt.

PER SERVE WITHOUT YOGHURT: 0 G FAT, 3 G DIETARY FIBRE, 735 KJ (175 CALS)

3 cups unsweetened apple juice
1 cup water
1 cup dried apricots
½ cup dried apples
½ cup sultanas
1 piece cinnamon stick, about 6 cm long
8 cloves
3 tbsp rice or sago
200 g low-fat natural yoghurt for garnish (optional)

 SERVES 6

BARBECUES

Barbecues fit with the Aussie lifestyle and provide an easy, friendly, casual way to eat. Unfortunately, many barbecues end up contributing lots of fat. But barbecues don't have to be fatty, and it's easy to turn on barbecued foods that are a waist watcher's delight.

TIPS

Choose lean meats rather than sausages. Lean meats cost more per kilo but you can make up for this by cutting the quantity and serving more vegetables or salads.

Add flavour to lean meats, seafood and skinless chicken by using marinades. Base a marinade on red wine, flavoured vinegars or citrus juices and add a little brown sugar or honey and some herbs for extra flavour.

When meat or chicken are barbecued, small quantities of cancer-causing compounds called heterocyclic amines form. Marinating meat for as little as 5 minutes in a mixture that includes some kind of sugar prevents these compounds forming.

Barbecue more seafood and less meat.

Barbecue vegetables such as zucchini (halved lengthwise), slices of eggplant, halved tomatoes, whole mushrooms, cobs of corn (wrap in foil), potatoes (wrap in foil), whole or halved onions, whole heads of garlic and seeded half capsicums.

Always preheat the barbecue before adding foods.

To stop chicken sticking to the barbecue, first cook it on High in the microwave for 3–5 minutes (the time depends on whether you are using small or large pieces), then barbecue as usual.

BARBECUED ZUCCHINI KEBABS

Pick firm zucchini and small squash for this recipe.

1. Soak the skewers in water for 30 minutes. This prevents them burning. Alternatively, use metal skewers.
2. On each skewer, thread 2 chunks zucchini, 1 mushroom, 2 pieces of yellow squash, 2 pieces of capsicum and 1 cherry tomato.
3. Combine all the marinade ingredients in a shallow dish. Brush the skewers with the marinade and grill or barbecue for 5 minutes, turning often.

PER SERVE: 2 G FAT, 6 G DIETARY FIBRE, 380 KJ (90 CALS)

8 *bamboo skewers*
4 *dark green zucchini,*
   each cut into 4 chunks
8 *button mushrooms*
8 *small yellow button*
   squash, halved
1 *red capsicum, seeded,*
   cut into 16 squares
8 *cherry tomatoes*

Marinade
1 *tbsp honey*
2 *tbsp balsamic vinegar*
2 *tbsp orange juice*
2 *tsp finely chopped ginger*
1 *clove garlic, crushed*
1 *tsp sesame oil*

 SERVES 4

BARBECUED GREEN SHALLOTS WITH ROMESCO SAUCE

Prepare to get your fingers dirty and enjoy the sweet succulence of green shallots. Try to find fat green shallots for this recipe.

40–50 green shallots

Sauce
olive oil spray
1 medium onion, peeled
    and cut in half
4 large cloves garlic
2 red capsicums
2 large tomatoes
2 tbsp almonds
1 tsp paprika
1 thick slice of Italian-
    style white bread,
    crusts removed,
    broken into pieces
freshly ground
    black pepper
2 tbsp red wine vinegar

 SERVES 6

To make sauce

1. Preheat the oven to 250°C and spray an oven tray with the olive oil spray.
2. Place the onion and garlic onto one half of the oven tray and spray them lightly with olive oil. Place the capsicums directly onto an oven shelf and put the oven tray on the shelf below so that the capsicums sit over the empty part of the tray (which will catch any juices). Reduce the oven temperature to 220°C and cook for 35 minutes. Lift the capsicums into a bowl and put the bowl inside a plastic bag. When cool enough to handle, peel the capsicums, collecting the juices. Strain out the seeds from the juice, and keep the juice.
3. Skin the tomatoes by removing their cores and cutting a small cross in the end. Then place the tomatoes in a bowl, cover with boiling water, leave for 30 seconds and drain. The skin will peel off easily.
4. Place the capsicum flesh, the onion, the flesh squeezed from the garlic cloves, the tomatoes, almonds, paprika, bread, pepper and vinegar in a food processor. Process until smooth, adding the reserved capsicum juices to thin the sauce. Store in the refrigerator until required.

Cooking the shallots

Cook the shallots on the barbecue until soft and blackened on the outside (this usually takes about 10 minutes). To eat, peel back the blackened outside skin and dip the onions into the romesco sauce.

PER SERVE: 3 G FAT, 5 G DIETARY FIBRE, 430 KJ (105 CALS)

BARBECUED EGGPLANT, CAPSICUM AND LEEKS

Try these at your next barbecue.

1. Cut four 40 cm long pieces of foil. Spray each with the olive oil spray and place 2 slices of eggplant, 2 pieces of capsicum and 2 lengths of leek on each one. Spray the vegetables with olive oil spray, sprinkle with the garlic and top with the rosemary. Wrap to form parcels and barbecue over a medium heat for 20–25 minutes. Serve with any barbecued meat, fish or chicken.

PER SERVE: 2 G FAT, 5 G DIETARY FIBRE, 230 KJ (55 CALS)

cooking foil
olive oil spray
1 eggplant, stem removed, cut into 8 slices
1 red capsicum, seeded, cut into 8 pieces
2 large leeks, washed and cut in half lengthwise and crosswise
2 cloves garlic, crushed
4 pieces fresh rosemary, about 8 cm long

 SERVES 4

BARBECUED MUSHROOMS

There is no better way to discover the wonderful flavour of mushrooms than this.

cooking foil
8 large flat mushrooms, or 16 smaller button mushrooms
olive oil spray
2 tsp finely grated lemon peel
2 tbsp chopped parsley
8 small bay leaves

1. Cut 4 pieces of foil, each large enough to hold 2 flat mushrooms, and spray with olive oil spray. Place the mushrooms on the foil and sprinkle with the lemon peel and parsley. Top with the bay leaves. Fold the parcels and barbecue for 15 minutes.

PER SERVE: 1 G FAT, 3 G DIETARY FIBRE, 120 KJ (30 CALS)

 SERVES 4

BARBECUED ASPARAGUS

Serve with barbecued meat, chicken or fish.

2 bunches asparagus
2 tsp olive oil
1 tbsp lemon juice
2 tsp honey
2 tsp Dijon mustard
black pepper

1. Trim the ends from the asparagus. In a shallow dish, combine the oil, lemon juice, honey, mustard and pepper. Add the asparagus and toss to combine. Cover and refrigerate for at least 10 minutes. Cook on a hot barbecue plate for about 2 minutes, turning once.

PER SERVE: 3 G FAT, 2 G DIETARY FIBRE, 220 KJ (55 CALS)

 SERVES 4

BARBECUED FENNEL

This is especially good with lamb.

1. Cut two squares of foil, each large enough to hold one fennel bulb. Spray with olive oil spray and sprinkle with garlic and sugar. Cut each fennel bulb in half lengthways and place 2 halves, cut side down, on each piece of foil. Top with lemon slices and wrap into parcels. Place on the barbecue and cook for 20–30 minutes. If desired, discard the lemon slices before serving.

PER SERVE: 1 G FAT, 5 G DIETARY FIBRE, 220 KJ (55 CALS)

cooking foil
olive oil spray
2 cloves garlic, crushed
2 tsp brown sugar
2 small fennel bulbs,
    about 250 g each,
    stalks trimmed to
    5 cm above bulb
2 lemons, sliced

 SERVES 4

BARBECUED SPICY CHICKEN

Skinless chicken thighs are moist and have excellent flavour.

1. Combine the yoghurt, garlic, curry paste and lime juice in a shallow bowl. Place the chicken thighs into the mixture and turn the chicken to coat it with the yoghurt mixture. Refrigerate for at least 30 minutes, preferably longer.
2. Remove the thighs from the marinade and barbecue for 15–20 minutes, turning once and spooning any remaining marinade over them as they cook.
3. For the sauce, combine yoghurt, mint, coriander and lime juice.
4. Serve the chicken topped with a dollop of sauce. Steamed rice or flat bread and a green salad go well.

PER SERVE: 7 G FAT, 1 G DIETARY FIBRE, 1110 KJ (265 CALS)

1 cup natural
   low-fat yoghurt
2 cloves garlic, crushed
2 tbsp green curry paste
2 tbsp lime juice
600 g skinless chicken
   thighs, trimmed of fat

Sauce
1 cup natural
   low-fat yoghurt
½ cup chopped
   fresh mint
½ cup chopped
   fresh coriander
1 tbsp lime juice

 SERVES 4

CITRUS CHICKEN LEGS

Use grapefruit, mandarin or orange in this recipe, which can also be cooked in the oven for 35 minutes at 180°C.

8 skinless chicken legs
2 cloves garlic
1 tbsp green peppercorns
1 cup grapefruit, orange or mandarin juice
1 cup chopped parsley
1 grapefruit, 1 orange or 2 mandarins, peeled and segmented

1. Place the chicken legs in a shallow dish.
2. Place the garlic, peppercorns, juice and parsley in a blender and process until combined. Pour over the chicken and refrigerate for at least 30 minutes (or overnight).
3. Remove the chicken legs from the marinade and barbecue for about 25–30 minutes over a gentle heat, brushing the chicken several times with the marinade. Serve garnished with the citrus segments.

PER SERVE: 7 G FAT, 1 G DIETARY FIBRE, 790 KJ (190 CALS)

 SERVES 4

BARBECUED CHICKEN KEBABS

You can buy chicken kebabs already marinated but these taste better and are much healthier.

1. Soak the skewers in cold water so they won't burn (or use metal skewers).
2. Place the chicken in a bowl and pour over the pasta sauce. Leave to marinade for 10 minutes.
3. Thread the chicken, mushrooms and capsicum onto the skewers and barbecue for 10–12 minutes, turning several times and brushing with the pasta sauce.

Serve with noodles and a green salad.

8 bamboo skewers
600 g skinless chicken breast, cut into 2.5 cm pieces
1 cup bottled tomato and eggplant pasta sauce
16 button mushrooms
1 red or green capsicum, seeded and cut into 3 cm cubes

PER SERVE: 4 G FAT, 4 G DIETARY FIBRE, 990 KJ (235 CALS)

 **SERVES 4**

BRANDIED CHICKEN WITH LIME, HONEY AND ROSEMARY

Use lemon if you don't have any limes. By removing the visible fat and the thick skin at the neck and rear end of a chicken, you lose more than half its fat.

1. Using kitchen scissors or a sharp knife, split the chickens down the centre and flatten them by giving them a good thump. Pull off any visible fat under the skin and remove the skin completely from the rear and neck ends of the birds. Cut off the wing tips.
2. Combine the peel, juice, rosemary, garlic, soy sauce, honey and brandy. Brush over both sides of the chickens, cover and refrigerate for at least an hour (or overnight).
3. Barbecue the chickens over a moderate heat, brushing them with the marinade mixture several times until cooked on both sides. (Cooking times vary. If you have a barbecue with a hood, the chickens will take about 25–30 minutes; on a regular barbecue they may take 40–45 minutes.)

*2 small (size 9 or 10)
or 1 large (size 16
or 17) chicken
finely grated peel and
juice of 1 lime
¼ cup finely chopped
fresh rosemary
2 cloves garlic, crushed
1 tbsp salt-reduced
soy sauce
1 tbsp honey
½ cup brandy*

PER SERVE: 7 G FAT, 1 G DIETARY FIBRE, 1230 KJ (295 CALS)

 SERVES 4

CHICKEN 'N' CHILLI BURGERS

Chicken burgers are delicious and filling. They're also good cold the next day for lunch. Use a food processor to make the crumbs, grate the vegetables and combine all the ingredients.

2 slices wholemeal bread
1 zucchini, grated
1 medium carrot, grated
400 g minced chicken
1 egg
1 tsp chopped fresh chilli
2 tbsp lemon juice
4 hamburger buns,
    preferably wholemeal
2 tbsp fruit chutney
2 medium tomatoes, sliced
8 slices cucumber
4 lettuce leaves

 SERVES 4

1. Using a food processor or blender, make the bread into crumbs and grate the zucchini and carrot. Combine the breadcrumbs, vegetables, chicken, egg, chilli and lemon juice. Form into 4 patties. Refrigerate for about 30 minutes before cooking, if possible.
2. Barbecue the chicken burgers for about 10–12 minutes, turning once.
3. Split and toast the buns. Spread the chutney on one half, top with a chicken burger, tomatoes, cucumber, lettuce and the remaining half bun.

PER SERVE: 7 G FAT, 4 G DIETARY FIBRE, 1040 KJ (250 CALS)

EASTERN LAMB BURGERS — SEE PAGE 88

HERBED FILLET STEAK — SEE PAGE 91

BARBECUED BASIL FISH WITH FRESH TOMATO SALSA — SEE PAGE 93

HONEY PRAWNS WITH SPICED SESAME SEEDS — SEE PAGE 98

MINTED LAMB KEBABS

There are now wonderful lean cuts of lamb that are tender and full of flavour. Without bones or skin, they are also quick to prepare.

1. Soak the skewers in cold water so they won't burn (or use metal skewers).
2. In a bowl, combine the mint, shallots, mint jelly, wine and pepper. Add the lamb and stir to coat the pieces with the marinade. Cover and refrigerate for about 20 minutes.
3. Thread the lamb onto the skewers and barbecue, turning and brushing with the marinade several times. Do not overcook. Serve with the wedges of lemon.

PER SERVE: 5 G FAT, 0 G DIETARY FIBRE, 910 KJ (220 CALS)

8 bamboo skewers
½ cup chopped
  fresh mint
½ cup sliced
  green shallots
½ cup mint jelly
  (home-made or
  purchased)
¼ cup red wine
freshly ground
  black pepper
600 g lean boneless
  lamb fillet or steaks,
  cut into 2.5 cm
  pieces
4 lemon wedges

 SERVES 4

EASTERN LAMB BURGERS

Buy lean lamb and ask the butcher to mince it for you, or use a food processor to mince it at home.

1 cup bulgur

1 cup boiling water

350 g minced lean lamb

½ cup chopped
   green shallots

½ cup chopped
   fresh mint

1 tbsp ground coriander

¼ cup lemon juice

½ cup low-fat
   natural yoghurt

1 tbsp chopped mint

1 tbsp chopped parsley

4 pita breads

1 large tomato, diced

1 cup alfalfa sprouts

1. Place the bulgur in a basin, pour boiling water over it, cover and leave for 10 minutes or until the water has been absorbed.
2. Combine the soaked bulgur, lamb, shallots, mint, coriander and lemon juice. Make into 4 patties, flatten slightly and barbecue on each side for about 5–8 minutes, or until brown.
3. Combine the yoghurt, mint and parsley.
4. Place the cooked lamb burgers into the pita bread, top with the tomato and sprouts and add a dollop of the minted yoghurt. Serve at once.

PER SERVE: 5 G FAT, 10 G DIETARY FIBRE, 1710 KJ (410 CALS)

 SERVES 4

PORK AND VEGETABLE KEBABS

The vegetables make this an interesting kebab.

1. Soak the skewers in cold water so they won't burn (or use metal skewers).
2. Combine the orange juice and hoisin sauce and pour over the pork. Cover and refrigerate for 30 minutes.
3. Thread the pork, mushrooms, tomatoes, zucchini and capsicum onto the skewers. Barbecue for 10–12 minutes, brushing with any remaining marinade and turning several times.

PER SERVE: 4 G FAT, 5 G DIETARY FIBRE, 970 KJ (230 CALS)

8 bamboo skewers
½ cup orange juice
2 tbsp hoisin sauce
500 g lean pork fillet
12 button mushrooms
12 cherry tomatoes
4 zucchini, cut
  into chunks
1 red capsicum, seeded
  and cut into
  3 cm cubes

 SERVES 4

BARBECUED VEAL, APPLE AND PRUNE BURGERS

Veal is lean, so take care not to overcook these burgers or they will be dry.

400 g minced veal
½ cup chopped
   pitted prunes
1 large apple, cored
   and grated
1 egg
1 cup cooked
   brown rice
½ cup chopped
   green shallots
2 tbsp mango chutney

Sauce
1 cup white wine
2 apples, peeled, cored
   and chopped finely
1 tsp cornflour
2 tbsp lemon juice

 SERVES 4

1. Combine the veal, prunes, apple, egg, rice, shallots and chutney and mix well. Form into 4 patties and flatten slightly. Barbecue over a medium heat for 5–6 minutes on each side, or until cooked.
2. While the patties are cooking, make the sauce. Heat the wine and add the apples, then cover and simmer for 3–4 minutes or until the apples are soft.
3. Combine the cornflour and the lemon juice and stir into the apple mixture to thicken slightly.
4. Serve the patties with the sauce. Steamed new potatoes and a green vegetable or salad make good accompaniments.

PER SERVE: 5 G FAT, 5 G DIETARY FIBRE, 1330 KJ (320 CALS)

HERBED FILLET STEAK

Fillet steak is expensive but better value than cheap cuts because you only need a small piece. To accompany, barbecue some potatoes wrapped in foil and serve with plenty of salad.

1. Combine the rosemary, parsley, chives, garlic and mustard and spread the mixture over both sides of the steaks. Barbecue for 5–6 minutes, turning once only and brushing with any remaining herb mixture. Serve with vegetables or salad and potatoes baked in foil.

PER SERVE: 5 G FAT, 1 G DIETARY FIBRE, 670 KJ (160 CALS)

1 tbsp chopped
   fresh rosemary
1 tbsp chopped
   fresh parsley
1 tbsp chopped
   fresh chives
2 cloves garlic, crushed
1 tbsp wholegrain mustard
4 lean fillet steaks, about
   120 g each

 SERVES 4

SPICY FISH

Use this marinade with fish or prawns.

200 g low-fat
   natural yoghurt
2 tbsp lime or lemon juice
¼ cup chopped coriander
   roots and leaves
2 cloves garlic, crushed
1 tsp ground cumin
2 tsp ground coriander
1 tsp fresh chopped chilli
4 fish cutlets (blue-eye,
   kingfish, salmon),
   about 700–750 g
4 lime or lemon wedges

1. Combine the yoghurt, lime juice, coriander, garlic, cumin, ground coriander and chilli and spoon over the fish. Cover and refrigerate for 15 minutes or longer.
2. Remove the fish from the marinade and barbecue for 2–4 minutes on each side, depending on the thickness of the fish fillets. Brush with any remaining marinade while cooking. Serve with the lime or lemon wedges.

PER SERVE: 2 G FAT, 1 G DIETARY FIBRE, 970 KJ (230 CALS)

 SERVES 4

BARBECUED OCEAN TROUT WITH DILL SAUCE

Use either Tasmanian ocean trout or Tasmanian Atlantic salmon. Keep the heat low and don't overcook these beautiful fish.

4 ocean trout steaks,
    about 700 g
olive oil spray
2 tbsp chopped dill

Sauce
½ cup white wine
2 tbsp lemon juice
1 tbsp chopped chives
150 g low-fat yoghurt
1 tsp Dijon-style mustard
1 tbsp chopped dill

1. To make the sauce, heat the wine, juice and chives and simmer until reduced by half. Strain the liquid, discarding the chives, and stir the liquid into the yoghurt. Add the mustard and dill and stir well.

2. Spray the ocean trout with oil and press the dill into both sides of the fish. Barbecue for no more than 2 minutes on each side. Serve with the sauce.

PER SERVE: 5 G FAT, 0 G DIETARY FIBRE, 890 KJ (215 CALS)

 SERVES 4

SIMPLY STUNNING SNAPPER

Nothing could be more simple than this easy recipe.

cooking foil
4 individual sized
    snapper
2 lemons
bunch fresh lemon
    thyme (or use dill,
parsley or a mixture
    of fresh herbs)

1. Cut 4 pieces of non-stick foil, each large enough to envelope one fish.

2. Cut the lemons in half and place half a lemon and a quarter of the lemon thyme inside each fish. Wrap the foil to enclose each fish. Barbecue for 15–20 minutes, or until the fish flakes easily with a fork. (The cooking time depends on the type of barbecue and is shorter if using a hooded barbecue.) Serve the fish from the foil.

PER SERVE: 2 G FAT, 0 G DIETARY FIBRE, 920 KJ (220 CALS)

 SERVES 4

BARBECUED BASIL FISH WITH FRESH TOMATO SALSA

An easy way to cook any type of fish, adding flavour but no fat.

1. Combine the dressing, lime rind, juice and basil and pour over the fish. Cover and refrigerate for 15 minutes, or longer.
2. While the fish is marinating, make the salsa. Bring a saucepan of water to the boil. Place the tomatoes into a bowl and pour the boiling water over them. Leave for 20 seconds, then drain. Peel the tomatoes and cut them into small dice. Combine the tomatoes, onion, basil and lime juice and mix well.
3. Barbecue the fish for 3–5 minutes, brushing with the marinade, until just cooked. Serve the fish with the salsa.

PER SERVE: 2 G FAT, 3 G DIETARY FIBRE, 950 KJ (225 CALS)

¼ cup no-fat or low-Joule dressing
2 tsp finely grated lime rind
2 tbsp lime juice
2 tbsp chopped fresh basil
4 fish cutlets (kingfish, blue-eye, ocean perch, gemfish), about 700–750 g

Salsa
500 g ripe red tomatoes, cores removed
1 small purple onion, finely chopped
½ cup finely chopped basil
1 tbsp lime juice

 SERVES 4

BARBECUED FISH WITH SPICY PINEAPPLE SALSA

A simple way to add flavour to fish. In summer, substitute mango for the pineapple.

1 clove garlic, crushed

*1 tsp finely
    chopped chilli*

*2 tsp chopped
    fresh ginger*

¼ cup lemon juice

2 tbsp teriyaki sauce

*4 boneless fish fillets
    about 700–750 g*

Spicy salsa

*1½ cups finely
    chopped fresh
    pineapple*

*1 small chilli, seeded
    and chopped finely*

*2 tsp chopped
    fresh ginger*

*1 cup torn fresh
    coriander leaves*

1. Combine the garlic, chilli, ginger, lemon juice and teriyaki sauce. Pour over the fish, cover and refrigerate for 15–20 minutes, turning the fish pieces once.
2. While the fish is marinating, make the salsa by combining the pineapple, chilli, ginger and coriander. Mix well and set aside.
3. Barbecue the fish until just cooked, brushing with the marinade and turning once. Serve with the pineapple salsa.

PER SERVE: 2 G FAT, 2 G DIETARY FIBRE, 940 KJ (225 CALS)

 SERVES 4

BARBECUED WHOLE FISH WITH LIME

A whole barbecued fish looks stunning. Coral trout, jewfish, ocean trout or snapper would all be excellent in this recipe.

1. Take a piece of foil large enough to encase the fish and lay half the lime leaves down the centre. Top with half the lemon grass and one third of the lime slices.
2. Brush the fish with the oil and lay on top of the lime slices. Place another third of the lime slices inside the fish and the rest of the lime slices on top of the fish. Add the rest of the lemon grass and the remaining lime leaves. Bring up the sides of the foil to make a parcel and barbecue for 25–30 minutes or until the fish flesh flakes easily.
3. While the fish is cooking, make the salsa by combining the lime juice, coriander, onion and cucumber. Serve the salsa with the fish.

PER SERVE: 3 G FAT, 3 G DIETARY FIBRE, 990 KJ (235 CALS)

cooking foil
about 10 lime leaves,
    if available
1 stalk lemon grass,
    white and green
    sections chopped
    roughly
2 limes, sliced
1 x 2 kg coral trout,
    cleaned and scaled
1 tsp macadamia or
    olive oil

Lime salsa
2 tbsp lime juice
½ cup coriander
1 small red onion,
    chopped finely
2 Lebanese cucumbers,
    diced finely

 SERVES 4

ORANGE AND SESAME SCALLOPS

Tasmanian scallops are delicious but delicate. Cook them for only a few minutes to keep them tender and moist.

4 long or 8 short
    bamboo skewers
½ cup orange juice
2 tsp finely grated
    orange rind
2 tsp chopped ginger
2 tbsp salt-reduced
    soy sauce
400 g Tasmanian
    scallops
16 button mushrooms
16 cherry tomatoes
1 tbsp sesame seeds
½ cup white wine
1 tsp cornflour
2 tbsp orange
    juice, extra

1. Soak the skewers in cold water so they won't burn (or use metal skewers).
2. Combine the orange juice, rind, ginger and soy sauce and pour over the scallops. Cover and refrigerate for 20–30 minutes.
3. Remove the scallops from the marinade and thread onto skewers with the mushrooms and cherry tomatoes. Sprinkle with the sesame seeds and barbecue over a gentle heat for 2–4 minutes, turning several times, until the scallops are just cooked.
4. While the scallops are cooking, place the marinade mixture into a small saucepan and bring to the boil. Add the wine. Combine the cornflour and extra orange juice and stir into the hot marinade mixture until thick. Serve the scallops with the sauce, accompanied by boiled rice and steamed green beans or a green salad.

PER SERVE: 2 G FAT, 3 G DIETARY FIBRE, 480 KJ (115 CALS)

 SERVES 4

BARBECUED OCTOPUS WITH TOMATO AND BASIL

Baby octopus cooks quickly but you need a really hot barbecue so it doesn't stew in its own juices.

1. Combine the lemon juice, chilli and garlic and add the octopus, tossing to combine. Cover and refrigerate for at least 1 hour.
2. While the octopus is marinating, combine the basil, tomatoes, capsicum, pepper and olive oil.
3. Barbecue the octopus until the tentacles curl and turn a pinkish colour. To serve, place the rocket on plates, top with the tomato mixture and then the octopus.

PER SERVE: 4 G FAT, 4 G DIETARY FIBRE, 730 KJ (175 CALS)

juice of 1 lemon
1 tsp finely
chopped chilli
1 clove garlic, crushed
500 g baby octopus,
cleaned, de-beaked
and cut in halves
1 cup chopped
fresh basil
3 large tomatoes,
diced finely
1 capsicum, seeded
and diced
freshly ground pepper
2 tsp extra virgin
olive oil
bunch rocket

 SERVES 4

HONEY PRAWNS WITH SPICED SESAME SEEDS

An excellent idea for a dinner party.

2 tbsp sesame seeds
2 tsp ground coriander
1 tsp ground cumin
1 tsp paprika
1 tbsp fennel seeds
2 tbsp honey
2 tbsp lime juice
2 tbsp hoisin sauce
1 tbsp salt-reduced
   soy sauce
1 kg green prawns

 SERVES 4

1. Toast the sesame seeds in a dry frying pan until they are golden brown (take care as they burn easily). Tip onto a plate to cool and then combine with the coriander, cumin, paprika and fennel seeds. Set aside.
2. Combine the honey, lime juice, hoisin sauce and soy sauce. Place the unpeeled prawns in this mixture, cover and refrigerate for at least an hour.
3. Barbecue the prawns in their shells until they turn pink. Each person peels his or her own prawns and dips them into the spiced sesame mixture.

PER SERVE: 5 G FAT, 2 G DIETARY FIBRE, 1230 KJ (295 CALS)

PRAWNS WITH HONEY AND RASPBERRY VINEGAR

A good recipe for entertaining. It is also simple and healthy.

1. Soak the skewers in cold water so they won't burn (or use metal skewers).
2. Remove the heads and shells from the prawns but leave the tails on. De-vein the prawns and place in a shallow dish.
3. Combine the garlic, onion, vinegar, lemon juice, honey and mustard and pour over the prawns. Cover and refrigerate for 30 minutes, or longer.
4. Thread the prawns and the capsicum onto skewers and barbecue until cooked, brushing with a little of the marinade mixture.
5. Heat any remaining marinade in a small saucepan and serve over the cooked prawns. Delicious with steamed rice.

PER SERVE: 2 G FAT, 2 G DIETARY FIBRE, 1000 KJ (240 CALS)

*4 long or 8 short
    bamboo skewers*
800 g green prawns
2 cloves garlic, crushed
*1 small onion,
    chopped finely*
3 tbsp raspberry vinegar
2 tbsp lemon juice
1 tbsp honey
*1 tbsp wholegrain
    mustard*
*1 yellow capsicum,
    cut into 3 cm
    squares*
*1 red capsicum, cut
    into 3 cm squares*

 SERVES 4

STIR-FRIES

Stir-frying is easy, healthy, economical and fast. It's also a great way to include lots of vegetables and use up whatever is in your vegetable crisper. For those who have previously allowed meat to dominate the dinner plate, stir-fries are a good way to reduce the amount of meat eaten without feeling too deprived. Use either a wok or a heavy-based, non-stick frying pan.

TIPS

To avoid using too much oil when stir-frying onion or other vegetables, place a large lid over the wok or frying pan for a minute or so to 'sweat' the vegetables and soften them.

Make sure the wok or frying pan is really hot before adding any oil. This allows you to swirl a very small amount of oil to coat the wok and prevent food burning.

Choose salt-reduced soy sauce to cut by more than half the sodium level of regular soy sauce.

Thai curry pastes are useful to add flavour. Their fat level varies from less than 1 to 5 g/tbsp so check the label, but even those with the highest level can usually be accommodated in a low-fat diet.

Freeze meat or chicken breast for 30 minutes or so before slicing. Using a sharp knife, it is then easy to slice the flesh very thinly. This helps the meat to cook quickly and stay tender.

To flatten pork, veal or chicken fillets so you can slice them thinly, place the meat between sheets of greaseproof paper and pound with the flat side of a meat mallet or an empty glass bottle.

STIR-FRIED BEEF WITH CHILLI AND GINGER — SEE PAGE 104

CHICKEN AND GREENS STIR-FRY — SEE PAGE 106

SUITABLE MEATS TO STIR-FRY

beef (rump, fillet or topside), sliced finely

lamb (lean back strap, fillet or lamb rump),
    sliced finely across the grain

pork (fillet) sliced

chicken (skinless breast or skinless thigh meat)

seafood (any kind of fish, prawns or strips
    of squid)

SUITABLE VEGETABLES

asparagus

bamboo shoots, canned

beans (green, yellow or snake)

bean sprouts (use fat mung bean sprouts
    and add at the end of cooking)

broccoli, sliced

Brussels sprouts, sliced

cabbage (any kind)

capsicum (green, orange, red or yellow)

carrot, sliced

cauliflower, sliced

celeriac, peeled and sliced

celery, sliced

chilli (any kind)

eggplant, sliced

fennel, sliced

garlic, crushed or sliced

green shallots

kohlrabi, peeled and sliced

leek, washed thoroughly and sliced

mushrooms (any kind), sliced

onion (any kind), sliced

pumpkin (any kind), peeled and sliced

radish (any kind), sliced

silver beet, washed and shredded

snow peas, strings removed

spinach, washed

squash, sliced

sugar snap peas, strings removed

sweet potato (orange flesh), peeled and sliced

sweetcorn, baby corn or kernels, fresh
    or canned

tomato, skin removed by dipping in boiling
    water for 30 seconds

zucchini, sliced

FOR FLAVOUR

chilli, sliced

ginger, sliced

fish sauce

garlic, crushed or sliced

herbs such as basil, coriander, dill, mint,
    parsley

lemon grass

lime juice

palm sugar (not more than 1 tsp)

sesame oil

soy sauce, preferably salt-reduced

Thai spice paste

STIR-FRIED BEEF WITH CHILLI AND GINGER

Omit the chilli for young children.

2 tsp sesame oil
1 large onion, peeled
    and cut into wedges
1 small red chilli
400 g lean rump steak,
    cut into strips (or
    buy ready-sliced beef
    strips)
250 g broccoli, sliced
200 g snow peas, sliced
1 red or yellow
    capsicum, seeded
    and sliced
2 tsp chopped
    fresh ginger
1 tsp palm sugar (or
    dark brown sugar)
1 tbsp salt-reduced
    soy sauce
juice of 1 lime (or lemon)
½ cup water

1. Heat a wok or large non-stick pan, add the sesame oil and cook the onion and chilli for 3–4 minutes over a gentle heat. Tip the onion into a bowl or plate.
2. Add the beef to the wok and cook over high heat, tossing frequently, for 3–4 minutes or until the beef is brown. Do not overcook.
3. Tip the onion back into the wok, add the broccoli, snow peas, capsicum and ginger and stir-fry for another 2–3 minutes.
4. Combine the sugar, soy sauce, juice and water and pour into the wok, stirring until the mixture boils. Serve at once with rice.

PER SERVE: 6 G FAT, 7 G DIETARY FIBRE, 930 KJ (220 CALS)

SERVES 4

STIR-FRIED LEMON CHICKEN WITH SPINACH

Use English spinach rather than silver beet.

1. Heat a wok or a large non-stick pan, add the oil, chicken and garlic and stir-fry for 4–5 minutes, or until the chicken begins to brown. Do not overcook.
2. Add the spinach, shallots and 2 tbsp of the chicken stock and stir-fry for about 1 minute or until the spinach wilts. Add the remaining chicken stock.
3. Blend the lemon juice with the cornflour and pour into the wok, stirring continuously. Simmer for 1 minute, then sprinkle with the basil and preserved lemon (if used). Serve with rice or noodles.

PER SERVE: 6 G FAT, 4 G DIETARY FIBRE, 830 KJ (200 CALS)

2 tsp olive oil

500 g skinless chicken breast fillet, cut into strips

2 cloves garlic, crushed

2 bunches English spinach (or 1 bunch silver beet), washed and shredded

1 cup sliced green shallots

¾ cup chicken stock

¼ cup lemon juice

2 tsp cornflour

½ cup chopped fresh basil

2 tbsp chopped preserved lemon (optional)

 SERVES 4

CHICKEN AND GREENS STIR-FRY

A great way to eat plenty of greens. Serve with a chunk of Turkish bread or with rice.

2 tsp olive or peanut oil

500 g skinless chicken
　　breast strips

1 tsp dried oregano

1 cup sliced spring
　　onions or green
　　shallots

2 cups sliced broccoli

2 cups sliced
　　green beans

1 cup sliced celery

1 bunch fresh
　　asparagus, cut into
　　4 cm lengths

1 cup chicken stock

1 cup fresh
　　chopped mint

1 punnet
　　cherry tomatoes

 SERVES 4

1. Heat a wok or a large non-stick pan, add the oil and stir-fry the chicken and oregano for 3–4 minutes, or until the chicken begins to brown. Do not overcook or the chicken will toughen.
2. Add the spring onions, broccoli, beans, celery and asparagus and stir-fry for 2–3 minutes.
3. Stir in the chicken stock and bring to the boil. Turn off the heat, add the mint and cherry tomatoes and serve at once.

PER SERVE: 6 G FAT, 7 G DIETARY FIBRE, 920 KJ (220 CALS)

CHICKEN WITH LEMON GRASS AND CORIANDER

If you can't find fresh lemon grass, it is now available chopped in jars.

1. Heat a wok or a large non-stick pan, add the sesame oil and stir-fry the lemon grass, garlic, chilli and onion over a moderate heat for 2–3 minutes.
2. Add the chicken and continue stir-frying for another 3–4 minutes. Sprinkle the peas into the wok and cook for another 2–3 minutes, or until the peas have thawed.
3. Gently stir in the tomatoes and simmer until they are hot but not mushy. Stir in the fish sauce and lime juice and serve at once over rice, topped with coriander.

PER SERVE: 9 G FAT, 8 G DIETARY FIBRE, 945 KJ (225 CALS)

2 tsp sesame oil

1 tbsp chopped fresh
   lemon grass root,
   white part only

2 cloves garlic, crushed

1 tsp chopped chilli

1 medium onion, sliced

400 g chicken thigh
   fillets, trimmed of fat

2 cups frozen peas

3 medium tomatoes,
   cored and cut
   into wedges

1 tbsp fish sauce

2 tbsp lime juice

1 cup chopped
   fresh coriander.

 SERVES 4

STIR-FRIED PORK WITH WATER CHESTNUTS

Try using oyster or shiitake mushrooms in place of regular mushrooms.

2 tsp sesame oil

1 medium onion, cut
 into wedges

1 clove garlic, crushed

500 g lean pork steak,
 cut into thin strips

2 tsp chopped
 fresh ginger

½ Chinese
 cabbage, sliced

2 x 170 g cans water
 chestnuts, drained
 and sliced

250 g mushrooms, sliced

1 tbsp salt-reduced
 soy sauce

1 tbsp oyster sauce

½ cup water

250 g mung bean sprouts

1. Heat a wok or a large non-stick pan, add the sesame oil and stir-fry the onion, garlic and pork for 3–4 minutes. Do not overcook.
2. Add the ginger, cabbage, water chestnuts and mushrooms and continue stir-frying for 2–3 minutes.
3. Combine the soy and oyster sauces with the water and stir into the pork and vegetable mixture. Add the bean sprouts and toss to combine. Serve at once with rice or noodles.

PER SERVE: 5 G FAT, 8 G DIETARY FIBRE, 1020 KJ (245 CALS)

 SERVES 4

BEEF AND MUSHROOMS

A lighter variation of the old favourite beef stroganoff.

1. Heat a wok or a large non-stick pan, add the oil and stir-fry the onion, garlic and steak for 3–4 minutes. Do not overcook. Add the mushrooms and continue stir-frying for 2–3 minutes.
2. Combine the red wine and tomato paste, add to the wok and simmer for 1 minute.
3. Blend the milk and cornflour and pour into the wok, stirring constantly until the mixture thickens. Sprinkle with the parsley and serve with flat noodles.

PER SERVE: 6 G FAT, 6 G DIETARY FIBRE, 1030 KJ (245 CALS)

2 tsp olive oil
1 large onion, sliced
2 cloves garlic, crushed
400 g lean rump steak, cut into thin strips
400 g mushrooms, sliced
1 cup red wine
½ cup tomato paste
1 cup evaporated skim milk
2 tsp cornflour
2 tbsp chopped parsley

 SERVES 4

STIR-FRIED LAMB AND FENNEL

Lean lamb is now available, making this an easy dish to prepare.

2 tsp olive oil
2 cloves garlic, crushed
400 g lamb steak, cut into strips
2 tsp dried dill
1 large fennel bulb, about 500 g, top removed and sliced
½ cup white wine
2 tbsp lemon juice
1 tsp cornflour
1 tbsp fresh chopped dill

1. Heat a wok or a large non-stick pan, add the oil and stir-fry the garlic, lamb and dill for 3–4 minutes. Add the fennel and continue stir-frying for 2–3 minutes.
2. Combine the wine, lemon juice and cornflour and add to the lamb, stirring constantly. Sprinkle with the fresh dill and serve with rice.

PER SERVE: 6 G FAT, 3 G DIETARY FIBRE, 700 KJ (165 CALS)

SERVES 4

CHILLI AND TOFU STIR-FRY

Tofu is a great foil for chilli.

2 tsp mustard oil (or use
  olive oil)

1 large onion, cut
  into wedges

1 small red chilli,
  chopped finely

2 tbsp Mexican spice
  seasoning (available
  in jars)

1 large red capsicum,
  seeded and sliced

420 g can red
  kidney beans

400 g can tomatoes,
  no added salt

300 g firm tofu, cut
  into 2.5 cm squares

2 tbsp chopped parsley

 SERVES 4

1. Heat a wok or a large non-stick pan, add the oil and stir-fry the onion, chilli, and Mexican seasoning for 2–3 minutes.
2. Add the capsicum and continue stir-frying for 2–3 minutes. Empty the undrained beans and tomatoes into the wok and heat until the mixture boils. Add the tofu and combine gently so it does not break up. Serve sprinkled with the parsley.

PER SERVE: 8 G FAT, 10 G DIETARY FIBRE, 980 KJ (235 CALS)

STIR-FRIED SEAFOOD

Vary the seafood according to what looks good at the fish market.

1. Heat a wok or a large non-stick pan, add half the oil (2 tsp) and stir-fry the garlic and onion over a low heat for 3–4 minutes. Add the chilli, ginger, snow peas and broccoli and stir-fry for 2–3 minutes. Tip the vegetables into a bowl.
2. Add the remaining oil to the wok. If using fish, stir-fry for about 3 minutes, or until the fish is white. If using octopus, add to the wok and cook over a high heat for 3–4 minutes, tossing frequently.
3. Add the prawns and vegetables to the wok and continue stir-frying until the prawns are pink. Sprinkle with the lemon juice and coriander and serve at once.

PER SERVE: 7 G FAT, 6 G DIETARY FIBRE, 1130 KJ (270 CALS)

1 tbsp olive oil

2 cloves garlic

1 large onion, sliced

1 tsp chopped
*   fresh chilli*

2 tsp chopped
*   fresh ginger*

2 cups sliced snow peas

2 cups sliced broccoli

500 g fish fillets, cut
*   into chunks (or use*
*   500 g cleaned baby*
*   octopus, halved)*

8 green king prawns,
*   shelled and*
*   de-veined*

2 tbsp lemon or
*   lime juice*

1 cup chopped
*   fresh coriander*

 SERVES 4

THAI FISH

Use any fish you prefer and remove the bones before cooking. Boneless fish fillets (usually shark) are excellent in this dish.

2 tsp sesame oil

1 medium onion,
  finely chopped

2 tbsp Thai red or
  green curry paste

1 medium eggplant,
  cut into strips

500 g fish fillets,
  cut into strips

1 bunch asparagus, cut
  into 4 cm lengths

1 red capsicum,
  seeded and sliced

1 yellow capsicum,
  seeded and sliced

½ cup light
  coconut milk

2 tbsp lime juice

1 tbsp fish sauce

½ cup basil leaves

1. Heat a wok or a large non-stick pan, add the sesame oil, onion, curry paste and eggplant and stir-fry for 4–5 minutes.
2. Add the fish, asparagus and capsicums and stir-fry for 3–4 minutes or until the fish flesh is opaque.
3. Stir in the coconut milk, lime juice, fish sauce and basil and heat through. Serve at once with rice.

PER SERVE: 7 G FAT, 4 G DIETARY FIBRE, 1030 KJ (245 CALS)

 SERVES 4

VEGETABLE AND PEANUT STIR-FRY

Use a mixture of any of the vegetables listed at the beginning of this chapter.

1. Heat a wok or a large non-stick pan, add the peanuts and toss until golden brown. Tip onto a plate and allow to cool.
2. Add the oil and ginger to the wok and stir briefly, then add the vegetables and stir-fry for 3–4 minutes or until tender crisp.
3. Combine the honey, sherry, soy sauce, lime juice and hoisin sauce. Add to the vegetables and stir well to combine. Serve with rice and sprinkle peanuts on top.

PER SERVE: 7 G FAT, 7 G DIETARY FIBRE, 600 KJ (145 CALS)

2 tbsp unsalted peanuts

2 tsp sesame oil

2 tsp finely
    chopped ginger

8–10 cups vegetables
    (for example,
    broccoli, cauliflower,
    carrot, Chinese
    cabbage, mushrooms,
    snow peas, zucchini)

2 tsp honey

¼ cup sherry (or
    orange juice)

1 tbsp salt-reduced
    soy sauce

2 tbsp lime juice

1 tbsp hoisin sauce

 SERVES 4

MAIN DISHES

Ideally, the main meal should be taken in the middle of the day when there is still plenty of time for the body to use the food that has been consumed. However, most people's working environment and lifestyle means the main meal is eaten in the evening. There's no reason why it can't be a stir-fry, a pasta or rice dish, soup, salad or a barbecue, so don't forget to look in these sections for ideas. Nor is there any reason why the main meal can't be vegetarian, so we have included a few meatless recipes too.

TIPS

Buy a lemon zester from a kitchenware shop to make it quick and easy to produce fine strips of citrus peel.

If you cannot resist the crisp brown fat on meat or the skin of chicken, cut it off before you cook it. Cold white lumps of fat don't tempt the tastebuds.

To stop pork, steak or chicken curling up while cooking, make some small snips around the edges with kitchen scissors before cooking.

Chicken breasts now grill well without drying out. This is because the flesh is left on the bone for 24 hours, giving an effect similar to the ageing of steak.

There is some evidence that the capsaicin in chilli can stimulate the metabolism and cause you to burn more kilojoules. However, it won't make up for a high-fat meal.

WARM THAI CHICKEN SALAD

A great summer dish that involves minimum cooking.

1. Combine the lime juice, soy sauce and coriander. Add the chicken and turn to coat with the marinade. Refrigerate for 30 minutes.
2. Remove the chicken from the marinade. Heat a non-stick frying pan, add the sesame oil and stir-fry the chicken for 4–5 minutes, or until just cooked.
3. Arrange the lettuce leaves on individual plates. Top with the shallots, carrot, radish, capsicum and chicken.
4. Make the dressing by combining the vinegar, sugar, sesame seeds, coriander, basil and Vietnamese mint. Spoon over the chicken and vegetables.

PER SERVE: 7 G FAT, 5 G DIETARY FIBRE, 840 KJ (200 CALS)

2 tbsp lime juice

1 tbsp soy sauce

½ cup chopped coriander

4 skinless chicken breasts, each cut into 4 pieces

2 tsp sesame oil

8 crisp lettuce leaves

12 green shallots, cut into fine strips

1 medium carrot, cut into fine strips

1 medium white radish, peeled and cut into fine strips

1 red capsicum, seeded and sliced finely

Dressing

¼ cup rice wine vinegar

1 tsp sugar

1 tbsp toasted sesame seeds

½ cup chopped fresh coriander

½ cup chopped fresh basil

2 tbsp chopped Vietnamese mint

 SERVES 4

BAKED CHICKEN WITH LEMON AND CARAMELISED ONIONS

This smells so good, you'll be licking your lips waiting for it to cook.

olive oil spray
8–12 skinless
   chicken legs
2 tbsp wholegrain
   mustard
finely grated peel and
   juice of 1 lemon
2 cloves garlic, crushed
1 tbsp balsamic vinegar

caramelised onions
1 tsp olive oil
500 g onions, peeled
   and sliced thinly
2 tbsp brown sugar
1 tbsp balsamic vinegar
½ cup red wine

 SERVES 4

1. Preheat the oven to 180°C. Spray a shallow casserole dish with the olive oil spray and arrange the chicken legs so they fit closely together.
2. Combine the mustard, lemon peel and juice, garlic and vinegar and spread over the chicken. Bake uncovered for 40 minutes, or until the chicken legs are tender and no pink colour runs when they are pierced with a skewer.
3. While the chicken is cooking, heat the olive oil in a saucepan, add the onions and brown sugar and cook over a moderate heat, stirring occasionally, for 15–20 minutes. Add the vinegar and wine and continue cooking for another 15 minutes, stirring occasionally. Serve the caramelised onions on top of the chicken.

PER SERVE: 8 G FAT, 3 G DIETARY FIBRE, 920 KJ (220 CALS)

CHICKEN AND VEGETABLE SPRING ROLLS

Good finger food to feed the family. Add chopped chilli for adults.

1. Cook the rice noodles according to the directions on the packet. Drain and rinse under cold water and drain again.
2. Combine the noodles, bean sprouts, snow peas, carrot, lime leaves, lime juice, fish sauce, chicken, peanuts and coriander. Mix well.
3. Fill a basin with moderately hot tap water. Dip each rice paper sheet into the water for about 1 minute to soften. Lay the rice paper on a flat surface. Place about 2 dessertspoonfuls of the filling mixture on each rice paper and roll up, tucking the ends in as you go. The moist rice paper will stick to itself. Place on a serving platter, seam side down.
4. For the dipping sauce, combine the water and sugar and stir until the sugar dissolves. Add the lime juice, soy sauce, coriander and mint and stir well.

PER SERVE: 4 G FAT, 4 G DIETARY FIBRE, 950 KJ (225 CALS)

100 g rice noodles

1 cup mung
 bean sprouts

1 cup sliced snow peas

½ cup grated carrot

4 kaffir lime leaves,
 finely shredded

1 tbsp lime juice

2 tsp fish sauce

1 cup chopped cooked
 chicken breast

2 tbsp chopped peanuts

2 tbsp coriander

12 rice paper sheets

Dipping sauce

1 tbsp boiling water

1 tsp brown sugar

2 tbsp lime juice

1 tbsp salt-reduced
 soy sauce

1 tbsp chopped
 coriander

1 tbsp chopped mint

 SERVES 4

CHICKEN IN POMEGRANATE MOLASSES

Pomegranate molasses is available from middle eastern food shops and some delicatessens. If you can't find it, substitute dark brown sugar.

2 tbsp pomegranate
   molasses
1 tbsp salt-reduced
   soy sauce
2 tbsp lemon juice
600 g chicken
   thigh fillets

1. Combine the molasses, soy sauce and lemon juice in a shallow ovenproof dish.
2. Trim the thigh fillets of all fat and place in the marinade, turning to coat each fillet. Refrigerate for 15 minutes, or longer.
3. Preheat the oven to 180°C. Place the dish containing the chicken thighs and the marinade in the oven and bake for 30 minutes, turning the thighs once. Serve with rice, noodles or potatoes and vegetables or a green salad.

 SERVES 4

PER SERVE: 6 G FAT, 0 G DIETARY FIBRE, 870 kJ (210 CALS)

GRILLED LAMB WITH RED CAPSICUM SAUCE

This is deliciously easy and very healthy. Serve with steamed new potatoes and either a green vegetable or a salad.

1. To make the sauce, preheat the oven to 250°C. Peel the onion and cut it in half across the centre. Place the onion and garlic on one half of an oven tray and spray them with olive oil spray. Place the capsicums directly onto the oven shelf and put the oven tray on the shelf below so that the capsicums sit over the empty part of the tray. Reduce the oven to 220°C and cook for 35 minutes. Place the cooked capsicums in a bowl and put the bowl inside a plastic bag. When cool enough to handle, peel the fine skin from the capsicums, discarding the seeds and collecting the juices. (It is easier to let the seeds collect with the juices and then strain them out.) Squeeze the garlic flesh into a food processor. Add the peeled capsicums, the onion and the vinegar and process, adding enough of the capsicum juices to give a sauce consistency.

2. While the capsicum is roasting, combine the lemon juice and mustard and rub over the lamb. Cover and refrigerate for 15 minutes (or longer, if desired).

3. Grill the lamb until cooked to your liking. Warm the sauce and serve each lamb steak on top of the sauce.

*4 lamb steaks, trimmed
   of all fat*
2 tbsp lemon juice
*2 tbsp wholegrain
   mustard*

Sauce
1 medium onion
½ head garlic
olive oil spray
2 red capsicums
1 tbsp balsamic vinegar

 SERVES 4

PER SERVE: 7 G FAT, 3 G DIETARY FIBRE, 1000 KJ (240 CALS)

LAMB SHANKS WITH LEMON

A hearty winter meal.

*4 lamb shanks, left
    whole, but trimmed
    of fat*
2 medium onions, sliced
*1 eggplant, about
    400 g, cut into
    2 cm cubes*
*250 g mushrooms,
    sliced*
1 tsp dried Italian herbs
*1 cup white wine
    (or water)*
*400 g can tomatoes,
    chopped roughly*
*3–4 pieces fresh
    rosemary*
2 lemons, sliced
1 large carrot, sliced
3–4 zucchini, sliced
*2 tbsp finely
    chopped parsley*

1. Preheat the oven to 180°C.
2. Using a stove-top casserole dish, brown the lamb shanks on all sides and then remove them from the pan. Add the onions, eggplant, mushrooms and herbs to the dish and cook, stirring occasionally, for 5 minutes. Replace the shanks and add the wine, tomatoes and rosemary. Place the lemon slices on top of the shanks, cover and bake for 1½ hours. Remove the rosemary. Add the carrot and zucchini to the casserole dish and bake for another 30 minutes. Serve topped with the parsley.

PER SERVE: 4 G FAT, 10 G DIETARY FIBRE, 1030 KJ (245 CALS)

 SERVES 4

LAMB SHANKS AND LENTILS

Another warming winter favourite.

1. Preheat the oven to 180ºC.
2. Place the coriander, cumin and cinnamon in a stove-top casserole dish and cook over a low–moderate heat for 1 minute, without burning.
3. Add the shanks, onion, eggplant, tomatoes and wine or water. Cover and bake for 1½ hours.
4. Add the lentils, mushrooms and water and bake, covered, for a further 30 minutes or until the lentils are cooked. Sprinkle with the lemon juice and mint and serve with steamed vegetables.

PER SERVE: 5 G FAT, 13 G DIETARY FIBRE, 1410 KJ (335 CALS)

1 tbsp ground coriander

2 tsp ground cumin

2 tsp cinnamon

*4 lamb shanks, trimmed
    of all fat*

1 large onion, diced

*1 medium
    eggplant, diced*

*800 g can tomatoes,
    chopped roughly*

*2 cups red or white
    wine (or use water)*

1 cup red lentils

250 g sliced mushrooms

1 cup water

2 tbsp lemon juice

2 tbsp chopped mint

 SERVES 4

LEMON VEAL

This is a really easy dish and you can use the same lemon mixture with skinless chicken thighs, pork steaks or rump steak.

*4 veal steaks, about
    700–750 g in total
1 whole lemon
1 clove garlic
2 tbsp fresh coriander
1 tbsp salt-reduced
    soy sauce
1 tsp brown sugar
water, as required*

1. Slice the lemon and remove the pips but do not peel. Place the lemon, garlic, coriander, soy sauce and sugar into a blender and process until well chopped, adding a little water if necessary.
2. Place the veal in a shallow ovenproof dish, pour the lemon mixture over, cover and refrigerate for at least 30 minutes.
3. Pre-heat the oven to 180°C. Bake the veal and lemon for 20–30 minutes or until the veal is cooked. Don't overcook. Delicious with rice and steamed vegetables or a green salad.

PER SERVE: 3 G FAT, 1 G DIETARY FIBRE, 850 KJ (205 CALS)

 SERVES 4

BRANDIED BEEF STEAKS

Fillet steak is ideal for this dish, but rump or a small lean T-bone is fine.

1. Combine the brandy, marmalade and ginger and spread over the steaks. Cover and refrigerate for at least 30 minutes.
2. Grill the steaks using a high heat for 3–4 minutes on each side, brushing frequently with the marinade. Delicious with steamed new potatoes, grilled tomato halves and a green salad.

PER SERVE: 6 G FAT, 0 G DIETARY FIBRE, 890 KJ (215 CALS)

¼ cup brandy
2 tbsp marmalade
1 tsp finely
* chopped ginger*
4 small pieces fillet
* steak, about 600 g*

 SERVES 4

SESAME PRAWNS AND ASPARAGUS

Excellent as a first course, or as a main meal.

2 limes

3 bunches asparagus,
  ends trimmed

3 tsp sesame oil

2 tsp finely chopped
  red chilli

3 tsp finely
  chopped ginger

1 kg green prawns,
  peeled (tails left on)
  and de-veined

2 tsp honey

1 cup white wine

1 tbsp salt-reduced
  soy sauce

1. Using a citrus zester or fine grater, grate the skin of the limes.
2. Boil water in a frying pan and cook the asparagus for 2 minutes. Drain and place the asparagus on a serving plate. Cover with foil to keep warm.
3. Heat the oil in a frying pan. Add the chilli, ginger and lime peel and stir over a moderate heat for 1 minute.
4. Add the prawns and cook for 1–2 minutes, or until they just turn pink. Arrange the prawns on top of the asparagus.
5. Add the honey, white wine and soy sauce to the frying pan. Bring to the boil, stir well and cook until slightly reduced. Drizzle over the prawns and serve at once.

PER SERVE: 3 G FAT, 2 G DIETARY FIBRE, 230 KJ (55 CALS)

 SERVES 6

SPICY FISH WITH LEMON YOGHURT

Easy to make and easy to eat. Tahini is sesame paste and it adds flavour and nutrients, as well as thickening the yoghurt.

1. Brush the yoghurt onto both sides of the fish.
2. Combine the chilli, turmeric, cumin, coriander, pepper and parsley and press the spicy mixture into both sides of the fish. Place on an oven tray lined with non-stick foil or baking paper. Cover and refrigerate for 15 minutes.
3. Preheat the oven to 180°C and bake the fish for 10 minutes or until the flesh flakes easily when pierced with a fork.
4. While the fish is cooking, combine the yoghurt, peel, juice and tahini and stir well. Serve the fish with the yoghurt sauce.

PER SERVE: 5 G FAT, 3 G DIETARY FIBRE, 1150 KJ (275 CALS)

4 boneless fish fillets
    (blue-eye, salmon or
    ling), about 750 g
    in total
¼ cup low-fat yoghurt
1 tsp dried chilli
1 tsp turmeric
1 tsp ground cumin
1 tbsp ground coriander
½ tsp ground
    black pepper
½ cup finely
    chopped parsley
200 g low-fat yoghurt
1 tbsp finely grated
    lemon peel
1 tbsp lemon juice
2 tsp tahini

 SERVES 4

127

TUNA BAKE

If preferred, you can substitute cooked lean mince or chicken for the tuna.

olive oil spray

400 g mushrooms,
    sliced finely

1 cup sliced
    green shallots

750 g jar good quality
    tomato pasta sauce

425 g can tuna, no
    added salt, drained

2 cups skim milk

2 tbsp plain flour

2 tbsp Parmesan cheese

2 eggs, beaten

pinch nutmeg

60 g (½ cup) grated
    reduced-fat cheddar
    (7 per cent fat)

1 tsp paprika

 SERVES 6

1. Preheat the oven to 180°C and spray an ovenproof casserole dish (approx 20 cm square) with olive oil spray.
2. Place half the mushrooms, shallots, tomato sauce and tuna into the casserole dish. Repeat the layers.
3. Beat the milk and flour together in a blender until smooth. Pour into a saucepan and stir constantly until the mixture boils and thickens. Add the Parmesan and allow to cool a little. Stir in the eggs and nutmeg and pour over the casserole. Sprinkle with the cheddar and paprika and bake for 30 minutes.

PER SERVE: 7 G FAT, 5 G DIETARY FIBRE, 1100 KJ (260 CALS)

ONION, POTATO AND SWEET POTATO FRITTATA

Leftover frittata is excellent served cold for lunch.

1. Place onions, sugar, vinegar and basil in a non-stick saucepan and cook over a low–moderate heat, covered, for 20 minutes, stirring occasionally.
2. Steam the potatoes and sweet potatoes for 15–20 minutes, or until just tender.
3. Preheat the oven to 180°C and line a 20 cm round cake tin with baking paper.
4. Slice the potatoes and arrange in layers in the cake tin with the onions.
5. Beat together the eggs, egg whites and milk. Pour the egg mixture over the vegetables, sprinkle the top with the cheese and bake for 30 minutes, or until firm.

PER SERVE: 4 G FAT, 5 G DIETARY FIBRE, 990 KJ (235 CALS)

3 large onions,
*   sliced thinly*
1 tbsp dark brown sugar
2 tbsp balsamic vinegar
1 tsp dried basil leaves
2 medium potatoes,
*   about 400 g, peeled*
1 orange sweet potato,
*   about 200 g, peeled*
2 eggs
3 egg whites
¾ cup skim milk
60 g (½ cup) grated
*   reduced-fat cheddar*
*   (7 per cent fat)*

 SERVES 4

VEGETABLES WITH PEANUT SAUCE

This dish takes a little time to prepare, but it is a complete meal. It is ideal for lunch or a light meal on a hot summer evening.

2 large potatoes, peeled

2 medium carrots, cut
   into julienne strips

2 cups broccoli pieces

400 g green beans,
   trimmed

1 red capsicum, seeded
   and sliced

1 green capsicum,
   seeded and sliced

1 long green cucumber

150 g mung
   bean sprouts

Sauce

2 tbsp chicken stock

1 medium onion,
   chopped finely

2 cloves garlic, crushed

1 tbsp tamarind puree

50 g (⅓ cup)
   crushed peanuts

1 tbsp crunchy peanut
   butter, no added salt

2 tbsp salt-reduced
   soy sauce

2 tbsp lemon juice

1 tsp chopped chilli

½ cup light
   coconut milk

1. To make the sauce, heat the chicken stock and gently cook the onion and garlic in the stock for 3–4 minutes. Add the tamarind, peanuts, peanut butter, soy sauce, lemon juice, chilli and coconut milk and simmer for 20 minutes, stirring occasionally and adding a little water if necessary to produce a thick sauce. While the sauce is cooking, prepare the vegetables.

2. Steam or microwave the potatoes until tender. Cut into thick slices. Place in the centre of a large platter.

3. Individually steam or microwave the carrots, broccoli and beans until barely tender. Drain into a colander and run under the cold tap so the vegetables remain crisp. Drain and arrange on a platter with the capsicum, cucumber and bean sprouts. Dot the sauce over the vegetables.

PER SERVE: 8 G FAT, 10 G DIETARY FIBRE, 830 KJ (200 CALS)

SERVES 6

CURRIED VEGETABLES

Use any vegetables you have for this simple dish. Chick pea flour is also called besan and is available from health food shops and some supermarkets.

1. Heat a frying pan, add the cumin and mustard seeds, cover and cook for a minute or two until they pop. Remove the pan from the heat and allow it to cool for a few minutes.
2. Add the oil, chilli, ginger, garlic, ground coriander and turmeric to the frying pan and cook over a gentle heat for 2–3 minutes.
3. Add the vegetables and water, cover and simmer for about 10 minutes.
4. Stir the chick pea flour into the yoghurt and then stir this into the vegetables. Do not boil or the yoghurt may curdle. Top with the coriander and serve with boiled rice.

PER SERVE: 4 G FAT, 9 G DIETARY FIBRE, 560 KJ (135 CALS)

1 tsp cumin seeds, preferably black cumin if you can find them
1 tsp black mustard seeds
2 tsp mustard seed or macadamia oil
1 tsp chopped chilli
3 tsp chopped ginger
2 cloves garlic, crushed
1 tbsp ground coriander
1 tsp turmeric
8 cups vegetables, cut into bite-sized pieces (choose from beans, broccoli, Brussels sprouts, capsicum, carrot, cauliflower, celeriac, eggplant, mushrooms, okra, onion, pumpkin, sweet potato)
½ cup water
200 g low-fat natural yoghurt
1 tsp chick pea flour
½ cup fresh coriander

 SERVES 4

Pizza

There are two options for healthy pizza. One is to buy the base—making sure it is bread, not pastry—and add your own topping. If you have the time, an even better choice is to start from scratch. Bread-making machines have a setting for pizza dough.

Pizza dough

1 sachet active dry yeast

1 ¼ cups lukewarm water

1 tsp sugar

1 ½ cups wholemeal flour

1 ½ cups plain flour

½ tsp salt

2 tsp olive oil

1. Combine the yeast, water and sugar and leave for 10–15 minutes until bubbles appear. (If there are no bubbles, the yeast is too old.)
2. Sift the flours, and salt and stir in the yeast mixture and the oil. Mix thoroughly, adding a little more flour if necessary to make a firm dough. Rub a little flour on your hands and knead the dough for about 10 minutes or until it is smooth and shiny, adding a little more flour if necessary. Place the dough into an oiled bowl and place a plastic bag over the bowl. Leave it in a warm place until the dough doubles in bulk (approximately 1 hour).
3. Punch the dough down, knead it well and place on a floured surface. Roll it out to a 30 cm circle and place on a greased pizza tray.
4. Top with filling, or place in the freezer until required. Defrost before adding the topping.

SEAFOOD PIZZA

1. Pre-heat the oven to 200°C.
2. Spread the tomato paste over the pizza dough and sprinkle with the oregano. Top with the onion, seafood, cheese and olives.
3. Bake for 20 minutes.

PER SERVE: 8 G FAT, 10 G DIETARY FIBRE, 2020 KJ (485 CALS)

1 pizza base
½ cup tomato paste
   (no added salt)
1 tsp dried
   oregano leaves
1 large onion sliced
   very finely
250 g seafood marinara
   mix (small prawns,
   scallops, mussels)
3 tbsp grated
   Parmesan cheese
8 black olives

SERVES 4

VEGETARIAN PIZZA

1 pizza base
2 tsp olive oil
1 medium onion, sliced
1 clove garlic, crushed
½ cup tomato paste (no
   added salt)
1 tsp dried oregano leaves
200 g sliced mushrooms
2 zucchini, sliced thinly
1 red capsicum, seeded
   and sliced finely
60 g (½ cup) grated
reduced-fat cheddar
   (7 per cent fat)
2 tbsp grated
   Parmesan cheese

1. Heat the oil in a saucepan and gently cook the onion and garlic for 5–6 minutes, stirring often so they do not brown.
2. Spread the pizza dough with the tomato paste and sprinkle with oregano. Spoon the onion onto the pizza and top with the mushrooms, zucchini, capsicum and cheeses.
3. Bake for 20 minutes.

PER SERVE: 10 G FAT, 12 G DIETARY FIBRE, 2020 KJ (485 CALS)

SERVES 4

POTATO AND ROSEMARY PIZZA

1 pizza base

½ cup tomato paste
  (no added salt)

2 tbsp fresh rosemary,
  finely chopped

2 large potatoes, peeled
  and sliced thinly

2 cloves garlic, crushed

 SERVES 4

1. Pre-heat the oven to 200°C.
2. Spread the tomato paste over the pizza dough and sprinkle with rosemary. Top with the potato and garlic.
3. Bake for 20 minutes.

PER SERVE: 7 G FAT, 11 G DIETARY FIBRE, 1940 KJ (460 CALS)

POTATO AND ROSEMARY PIZZA — SEE PAGE 134

LAMB SHANKS AND LENTILS — SEE PAGE 123

FETTA AND BABY SPINACH PIZZA

1. Pre-heat the oven to 200°C.
2. Heat the oil in a saucepan and gently cook the onions, garlic, rosemary and vinegar for 5–6 minutes, stirring often so they do not brown. Stir the mustard into the onions and spoon onto the pizza base. Top with the fetta.
3. Bake for 15 minutes.
4. Pile the spinach on top and serve at once.

PER SERVE: 8 G FAT, 11 G DIETARY FIBRE, 1920 KJ (460 CALS)

1 pizza base

2 tsp olive oil

2 large onions, sliced
   thinly

2 cloves garlic, crushed

2 tbsp fresh rosemary,
   finely chopped

2 tbsp balsamic vinegar

1 tbsp wholegrain
   mustard

100 g low-fat fetta
   (3 per cent fat),
   crumbled

200 g baby spinach
   leaves

 SERVES 4

VEGETABLES

Most people know that vegetables are good for you and most people intend to eat more of them. But vegetables have been sacrificed in a lifestyle that emphasises snacking, eating on the run and fast foods. You can't eat peas easily in the car! More than ever before, we know that vegetables are important not only for their fibre and vitamins, but because they contain literally hundreds of anti-cancer compounds. These compounds cannot be obtained from a pill. Studies using supplements to replicate the vitamins in vegetables have failed to show the same benefits gained from eating the real thing. Researchers now believe the active components in vegetables may need the presence of their hundreds of relatives to function correctly. So it's back to vegetables! (There are also some great vegetable recipes in the barbecue section of this book.)

A special word on potatoes. Potatoes are a great food. They are an excellent sources of vitamins, fibre and minerals, they taste good and fill you up. Contrary to old-fashioned ideas, spuds won't make you fat because, by themselves, they contain no fat. Unfortunately, potatoes are usually served with some type of fat. For example, chips are cooked in hydrogenated oil (or dripping, in the case of some fast food fries), roast potatoes soak up meat fat, mashed potatoes have butter or margarine, jacket potatoes are topped with sour cream. It's the fat that so often accompanies potatoes that causes weight problems, not the potatoes themselves. But you can cook potatoes so they keep their flavour and nutrients without adding lots of fat.

TIPS

Use a food processor to slice potatoes and onions quickly.

A head of garlic can be baked in some rice dishes. Simply place the head, with its skin left on, in the centre of a pilaf or paella. A delicate garlic flavour will pervade the rice and you can also squeeze out the soft creamy garlic when the dish is cooked.

Lemon juice will make green vegetables lose their colour, so add it at the table.

If a pumpkin is hard to peel, bake it in its skin and peel it when cooked.

To make Brussels sprouts more appealing, slice them and stir-fry in a little olive oil.

If kids don't like cooked vegetables, serve them raw.

The skin on capsicums makes some people burp. To remove the skin, roast the capsicums in an oven preheated to 220°C. Place a baking dish on the bottom shelf and put the capsicums on the oven shelf directly above the tray. Roast capsicums for 30 minutes or until the skin is blistered and is blackening. Remove the capsicums from the oven using tongs and place them in a plastic bag. Leave for 10 minutes, then peel and remove the seeds. Do not rinse, and catch the juices to use in sauces.

MUSTARD AND HERB POTATOES

Use desiree, pontiac, King Edward or Idaho potatoes for baking and stuffing.

1. Preheat the oven to 180°C.
2. Place the potatoes on an oven shelf and bake for about 1¼ hours, or until tender when pierced with a skewer. Alternatively, cook the potatoes on High in a microwave for 12–15 minutes. Using tongs, remove the potatoes, cut a lid from each and scoop out some of the flesh.
3. Mash the scooped flesh and add the mustard, basil, mint, chives, yoghurt and pepper. Pile the potato mash back into the potato shells and bake for a further 15 minutes, or microwave for 4–5 minutes.

PER SERVE: 1 G FAT, 4 G DIETARY FIBRE, 650 KJ (155 CALS)

*4 medium potatoes,
about 200 g each,
scrubbed*
*1 tbsp wholegrain
mustard*
*½ cup chopped
fresh basil*
1 tbsp chopped mint
1 tbsp chopped chives
*½ cup low-fat
natural yoghurt*
*freshly ground
black pepper*

 SERVES 4

Spinach stuffed spuds

Spinach tastes great when it's stuffed into spuds. English spinach has a milder flavour than silver beet.

4 medium potatoes,
   about 200 g each,
   scrubbed
½ bunch
   English spinach
½ cup low-fat
   natural yoghurt
pinch nutmeg
2 tbsp chopped
   green shallots
1 tbsp lemon juice

1. Preheat the oven to 180°C.
2. Place the potatoes on an oven shelf and bake for about 1¼ hours, or until tender when pierced with a skewer. Alternatively, cook the potatoes on High in a microwave for 12–15 minutes. Using tongs, remove the potatoes, cut a lid from each and scoop out some of the flesh.
3. While the potatoes are baking, wash and steam the spinach for 1–2 minutes or until it wilts. Cool and squeeze tightly to remove as much water as possible. Chop finely.
4. Mash the potato flesh and combine with the spinach, yoghurt, nutmeg, shallots and lemon juice. Pile back into the potato shells and bake for 15 minutes, or microwave on High for 4–5 minutes.

SERVES 4

PER SERVE: < 1 G FAT, 5 G DIETARY FIBRE, 650 KJ (155 CALS)

POTATOES WITH DRIED TOMATOES AND MUSHROOM

Use dried tomatoes from the vegetable section and reconstitute them rather than using dried tomatoes in oil.

1. Preheat the oven to 180°C.
2. Place the potatoes on an oven shelf and bake for about 11/4 hours, or until tender when pierced with a skewer. Alternatively, cook the potatoes on High in a microwave for 12–15 minutes. Using tongs, remove the potatoes, cut a lid from each and scoop out some of the flesh.
3. While the potatoes are cooking, place the dried tomatoes in a small bowl and cover with boiling water. Leave to stand for 15–30 minutes, then drain, reserving the water to use in pasta sauces. Cut the tomatoes into smaller pieces.
4. Mash the potato flesh and add the dried tomatoes, cottage cheese, pepper, basil and mushrooms. Pile the mixture back into the potato shells and bake for 15 minutes, or microwave on High for 4–5 minutes.

4 medium potatoes, about 800 g, scrubbed
12 dried tomatoes pieces
2 tbsp low-fat cottage cheese
freshly ground black pepper
2 tbsp chopped basil
1 cup finely chopped mushrooms

 SERVES 4

PER SERVE: 1 G FAT, 5 G DIETARY FIBRE, 670 KJ (160 CALS)

CHILLI AND CORIANDER STUFFED SPUDS

This is great with grilled chicken or barbecued fish and salad.

4 medium potatoes,
   about 800 g,
   scrubbed
½ cup finely
   chopped coriander
½ cup low-fat yoghurt
2 tsp chopped chilli

 SERVES 4

1. Preheat the oven to 180°C.
2. Place the potatoes on an oven shelf and bake for about 1¼ hours, or until tender when pierced with a skewer. Alternatively, cook the potatoes on High in a microwave for 12–15 minutes. Using tongs, remove the potatoes, cut a lid from each and scoop out some of the flesh.
3. Mash the potato flesh and add the coriander, yoghurt and chilli. Pile the mixture back into the potato shells and bake for 15 minutes, or microwave on High for 4–5 minutes.

PER SERVE: < 1 G FAT, 4 G DIETARY FIBRE, 620 KJ (150 CALS)

CRISPY POTATO PANCAKES

A great substitute for chips.

1. Grate the potatoes and onion using a coarse grater or a food processor. Using your hands, squeeze the potato and onion to extract as much moisture as possible.
2. Combine the grated vegetables with the flour, thyme, egg, egg white and pepper. Mix well, adding a little more flour if the mixture seems to be too wet (this depends on how much water you have been able to squeeze from the potatoes).
3. Heat a heavy-based frying pan and spray with the olive oil spray. Drop spoonfuls of the potato mixture into the pan and cook over a low–moderate heat for 3–4 minutes on each side. Remove the first batch of pancakes and keep them warm while cooking the remaining mixture.

750 g potatoes, scrubbed
1 medium onion
¼ cup self-raising flour
1 tsp dried thyme leaves
1 egg
1 extra egg white
freshly ground
*   black pepper*
olive oil spray

 **MAKES ABOUT 8 TO SERVE 4**

PER SERVE: 2 G FAT, 4 G DIETARY FIBRE, 770 KJ (185 CALS)

SPICY OVEN CHIPS

Another good substitute for chips.

baking paper
1 tbsp paprika
2 tsp cumin
¼ tsp black pepper
2 tbsp dried
*   parsley flakes*
750 g potatoes,
*   preferably King*
*   Edward, pontiac or*
*   desiree, peeled and*
*   cut into wedges*
olive oil spray

1. Preheat the oven to 210°C and spread a flat baking tray with a sheet of baking paper.
2. Place the paprika, cumin, pepper and parsley into a plastic bag. Add the potato wedges, hold the neck of the bag tight and shake to coat the potatoes with the spices. Arrange the potatoes in a single layer on the baking paper. Spray with the olive oil spray and bake for 25 minutes, or until the wedges are golden brown.

PER SERVE: 1 G FAT, 4 G DIETARY FIBRE, 570 KJ (135 CALS)

SERVES 4

POTATO AND ROCKET FRITTATA

This frittata is equally delicious served hot with a main meal or cold for the next day's lunch.

750 g potatoes, peeled
    and sliced thinly
2 large onions,
    sliced thinly
olive oil spray
1 bunch rocket,
    washed and sliced
4 eggs
2 egg whites
½ tsp ground
    black pepper

1. Steam or microwave the potato and onion slices until almost tender.
2. Heat a heavy-based frying pan, spray with olive oil spray and arrange the potato and onion slices and rocket in layers in the frying pan.
3. Beat the eggs, the egg whites and the pepper. Pour the egg mixture over the potato and cook over a low heat for 10–12 minutes, carefully lifting the potatoes and allowing the uncooked egg mixture to run underneath. When the eggs are almost set, place the frying pan under the griller to brown the top of the frittata. If serving cold, refrigerate until required.

PER SERVE: 6 G FAT, 5 G DIETARY FIBRE, 1000 KJ (240 CALS)

 SERVES 4

ROASTED CARAMELISED ONIONS AND JERUSALEM ARTICHOKES

Great with roast meat, there is no need to peel the artichokes in this recipe.

1. Preheat the oven to 200°C and heat a baking dish for 2–3 minutes. Pour the olive oil into the dish, add the onions and artichokes and mix well to spread the oil over the vegetables. Roast for 20 minutes, turning once.
2. Combine the sugar, lemon juice and soy sauce and pour over the onions and artichokes. Stir to mix and bake for another 10 minutes, stirring once. Serve piping hot.

1 tbsp olive oil
2 large onions,
    sliced thinly
500 g Jerusalem
    artichokes, scrubbed
2 tsp brown sugar
2 tbsp lemon juice
1 tbsp salt-reduced
    soy sauce

PER SERVE: 5 G FAT, 5 G DIETARY FIBRE, 450 KJ (110 CALS)

 SERVES 4

POTATO SOUFFLE

Easy to make and popular with all ages.

1. Steam or microwave the potatoes until tender. Peel and mash, adding the shallots, pepper, chives, milk and egg yolk. Leave to stand for 5 minutes.
2. Preheat the oven to 180°C and coat 4 individual souffle dishes with olive oil spray.
3. Beat the egg whites until stiff. Fold a little of the egg whites into the potato mixture and mix lightly, then gently fold in the remaining egg white. Do not beat too vigorously or the egg whites will lose their fluffiness. Spoon the mixture into the souffle dishes, sprinkle with the Parmesan and bake for about 20 minutes, or until risen and brown. Serve at once.

PER SERVE: 2 G FAT, 3 G DIETARY FIBRE, 680 KJ (160 CALS)

750 g potatoes
½ cup sliced
  green shallots
freshly ground
  black pepper
1 tbsp chopped chives
⅓ cup low-fat milk
1 egg yolk, beaten
olive oil spray
2 egg whites
1 tbsp finely grated
  Parmesan cheese

 SERVES 4

POTATO AND CELERY CAKE

Take leftovers to work the next day.

3 medium (about
   600 g) potatoes,
   peeled
1 medium onion
1 cup finely
   sliced celery
1 tbsp lemon juice
2 eggs, beaten
1 cup instant skim
   milk powder
2 tbsp chopped dill
olive oil spray
1 tbsp finely grated
   Parmesan cheese

 SERVES 4

1. Using a food processor, grate the potatoes and onion then use your hands to squeeze as much moisture out of the mixture as possible.
2. Mix the potatoes and onions with the celery, lemon juice, eggs, skim milk powder and dill.
3. Preheat the oven to 180°C and coat either a 20 cm cake tin or a muffin pan (for 4 large muffins) with olive oil spray. Press the potato mixture into the cake tin or muffin pan. Sprinkle the cheese over the potato mix and bake for 40 minutes for the cake or 25 minutes if using a muffin pan.

PER SERVE: 4 G FAT, 4 G DIETARY FIBRE, 1040 KJ (250 CALS)

RED AND GREEN CABBAGE WITH RAISINS AND POPPY SEEDS

Boiled cabbage is unappetising. Try this instead.

1. Heat the olive oil in a medium-sized saucepan and add the red and green cabbage, the raisins and apple juice. Cover and cook over a medium heat for about 4 minutes, stirring once or twice. Add the poppy seeds and toss well to combine.

PER SERVE: 3 G FAT, 8 G DIETARY FIBRE, 440 KJ (105 CALS)

2 tsp olive oil
4 cups shredded green cabbage
4 cups shredded red cabbage
¼ cup raisins
½ cup apple juice
2 tsp poppy seeds

 SERVES 4

HONEYED GINGER CARROTS

A good way to make carrots taste good.

500 g carrots, scrubbed and cut into thick matchstick pieces
2 tsp honey
2 tsp finely chopped ginger
2 tbsp orange juice
2 tsp finely grated orange peel

1. Steam the carrots for 5 minutes.
2. Combine the honey, ginger, orange juice and orange peel and stir over a low heat for 1 minute. Add the carrots and toss well to combine. Allow to stand for 2 minutes before serving.

PER SERVE: < 1 G FAT, 4 G DIETARY FIBRE, 190 KJ (45 CALS)

 SERVES 4

CARAMELISED ONIONS

Onions contain natural sugars. Serve these with grilled meats or as a topping for jacket potatoes.

1 tbsp olive oil
2 large onions,
  sliced finely
2 tbsp balsamic vinegar

1. Heat the oil in a saucepan, add the onions, cover and allow to sweat over a low heat for 30 minutes, stirring occasionally. Remove the lid, add the balsamic vinegar and increase the heat, stirring constantly until the onions are a rich brown.

SERVES 4 AS A VEGETABLE OR 6 AS A TOPPING FOR POTATOES

PER SERVE (FOR 4): 5 G FAT, 2 G DIETARY FIBRE, 280 KJ (65 CALS)
PER SERVE (FOR 6): 3 G FAT, 1 G DIETARY FIBRE, 190 KJ (45 CALS)

BEANS AND CORN

The amino acids in beans and corn make an excellent nutritional match. They also taste good together. If you prefer, start with 1 cup of dried kidney beans, soak them overnight, drain, cover with fresh water and boil for 40 minutes.

1. Empty the beans and their liquid into a saucepan, add the corn, chilli and sugar and stir over medium heat until hot. Add the parsley.

PER SERVE: 1 G FAT, 13 G DIETARY FIBRE, 890 KJ (210 CALS)

680 g can red
  kidney beans
250 g frozen corn
kernels or 400 g can
  corn kernels, drained
1 tsp chopped chilli
  (optional)
1 tsp brown sugar
½ cup chopped parsley

 SERVES 4

CAULIFLOWER WITH RICH TOMATO SAUCE

Substitute zucchini or broccoli for the cauliflower.

1. Cut the cauliflower into individual pieces and steam for 4–5 minutes or microwave in a covered container on High for 2 minutes. Do not overcook the cauliflower, it should be barely tender. Place the cauliflower in a shallow dish.

2. Heat the oil in a saucepan and cook the onion, garlic and chilli over a gentle heat for 3–4 minutes.

3. Using a blender or food processor, crumb the bread. Add the onion mixture, tomatoes, sugar, paprika, vinegar and pepper to the blender or processor. Blend to form a paste. Pour over the cauliflower and bake in a moderate oven for 10 minutes or heat in the microwave on High for 5–6 minutes, or until piping hot.

PER SERVE: 3 G FAT, 6 G DIETARY FIBRE, 440 KJ (105 CALS)

1 small cauliflower, or
  ½ a large one
2 tsp olive oil
1 medium onion,
  chopped finely
1 clove garlic, crushed
1 tsp chopped chilli
1 slice wholemeal bread
500 g fresh tomatoes,
  cored and
  chopped roughly
1 tsp brown sugar
1 tsp paprika
2 tbsp balsamic vinegar
freshly ground
  black pepper

 SERVES 4

SPICY BROCCOLI

Here's a simple way to add flavour to broccoli. Chilli and ginger are both available ready chopped in jars. This recipe is also good using cauliflower, Brussels sprouts, zucchini or potatoes.

*1 tbsp mustard or
   macadamia oil*
2 medium onions, sliced
2 cloves garlic
2 tsp chopped ginger
1 tsp chopped chilli
2 tsp coriander seeds
1 tsp cumin seeds
*500 g broccoli, trimmed
   and cut into
   small pieces*
½ cup water

 SERVES 4

1. Heat a non-stick frying pan or wok, add the oil, onions, garlic, ginger, chilli, coriander and cumin seeds, cover and cook over a low heat for 10–15 minutes, stirring occasionally, until the onions are soft.
2. Add the broccoli and water, cover and cook for 5 minutes, or until the broccoli is just tender.

PER SERVE: 3 G FAT, 7 G DIETARY FIBRE, 320 KJ (75 CALS)

Caramelised onions (served on a baked potato) — see page 148

ROASTED TOMATOES — SEE PAGE 155

SESAME SNOW PEAS AND BEANS

*Snow peas go well with green beans and sesame. Use honey snap peas if they are in season.
This is also a good way to cook halved Brussels sprouts.*

1. Steam the beans and snow peas for 2–3 minutes.
2. Heat a non-stick frying pan, add the sesame oil, seeds and garlic and stir-fry for a minute or two. Add the beans and peas and toss together.

PER SERVE: 3 G FAT, 6 G DIETARY FIBRE, 320 KJ (75 CALS)

*400 g green beans,
   topped and tailed*
*200 g snow peas,
   strings removed*
1 tsp sesame oil
1 tbsp sesame seeds
1 clove garlic, crushed

 SERVES 4

GARLIC BEANS AND SNOW PEAS

Excellent with frittata or grilled fish.

400 g green beans
150 g snow peas
*½ cup chicken or
   vegetable stock*
2 cloves garlic, crushed
*2 tsp finely grated
   lemon peel*
lemon wedges

1. Steam the beans and snow peas until just tender. Do not overcook. Drain and rinse immediately under the cold tap so the vegetables retain their green colour.
2. Heat the stock in a frying pan, add the garlic, lemon peel, beans and peas and stir thoroughly to reheat the vegetables. Serve with lemon wedges.

PER SERVE: 1 G FAT, 5 G DIETARY FIBRE, 200 KJ (45 CALS)

 SERVES 4

CARROTS, PARSNIP AND MUSHROOMS WITH LEMON DRESSING

Combine vegetables and add some flavour to make them more interesting. If you don't like parsnips, use extra carrot.

2 tsp olive oil
1 small onion, sliced
2 large carrots, cut into
   thin slices
1 large parsnip, peeled
   and cut into
   thin slices
½ cup chicken stock
250 g mushrooms,
   sliced
1 tbsp lemon juice
1 tbsp chopped mint

 SERVES 4

1. Heat the oil in a saucepan, add the onion, cover and cook over a gentle heat for 2–3 minutes, stirring once or twice. Add the carrots, parsnip and stock, bring to the boil, cover and simmer for 5 minutes.

2. Add the mushrooms and continue cooking with the lid off for a further 3 minutes, stirring occasionally. Add the lemon juice and mint, toss well and serve, pouring any remaining juice over the vegetables.

PER SERVE: 3 G FAT, 5 G DIETARY FIBRE, 340 KJ (80 CALS)

BRAISED LEEKS

Serve with grilled fish, or barbecued lamb, beef or chicken.

1. Trim away the top tough parts of the leeks, but do not trim off all the green section. If the leeks are large, cut them in half lengthwise. Wash thoroughly, opening the green leaves with your fingers to remove any dirt. If the leeks are too long to fit into the frying pan, cut them into shorter lengths.
2. Heat a large frying pan, add the oil and garlic and cook for 1 minute. Add the leeks, wine, peppercorns, bay leaves, rosemary and lemon peel and simmer, covered, for 15 minutes. Remove the bay leaves.
3. Place the leeks in a shallow serving dish. Add the lemon juice and honey to the cooking pan, heat and pour over the leeks.

PER SERVE: 3 G FAT, 3 G DIETARY FIBRE, 220 KJ (50 CALS)

2 large or 4 small leeks
2 tsp extra virgin
   olive oil
2 cloves garlic, crushed
1 cup white wine
10 peppercorns
2 bay leaves
1 tsp dried
   rosemary leaves
2 tsp finely grated
   lemon peel
2 tbsp lemon juice
1 tsp honey

 SERVES 4

RATATOUILLE

Delicious served hot or cold with some good bread.

12 baby eggplant, stalks removed and halved lengthwise

olive oil spray

1 red capsicum, seeded and sliced

500 g zucchini, sliced

4 large tomatoes, sliced

½ cup fresh basil, shredded

2 cloves garlic, crushed

 SERVES 4

1. Preheat the oven to 190°C.
2. Grill or barbecue the eggplant until brown.
3. Spray a casserole dish with the olive oil spray and place half the eggplant skin side down on the bottom. Cover with the capsicum, zucchini and tomatoes. Sprinkle with the basil. Cover with the remaining eggplant, skin side up. Sprinkle with garlic and spray lightly with olive oil spray. Cover tightly and bake for 30 minutes.

PER SERVE: 2 G FAT, 9 G DIETARY FIBRE, 380 KJ (90 CALS)

ROASTED TOMATOES

Roasting brings out the flavour in tomatoes. Eat them hot or keep in the fridge for 2–3 days and use them on toast or in sandwiches.

1. Preheat the oven to 180°C.
2. Place the tomatoes close together on an oven tray that will just hold them. Sprinkle with the sugar and spray with olive oil. Strew rosemary over the top and roast for 30 minutes. Cool and refrigerate, covered, until required.

12 tomatoes, preferably Roma, halved
2 tsp sugar
olive oil spray
fresh rosemary sprigs

PER SERVE: 1 G FAT, 2 G DIETARY FIBRE, 130 KJ (30 CALS)

 SERVES 6

GREEK-STYLE BEANS

In Greece, vegetables are not served raw or simply steamed, but are cooked in flavoursome juices that can be mopped up with plenty of good bread.

½ cup white wine
½ cup water
1 tbsp extra virgin olive oil
2 cloves garlic, crushed
2 bay leaves
1 tsp dried thyme
2 sprigs fresh rosemary
2 tbsp lemon juice
12 baby onions, peeled
500 g green beans
200 g button mushrooms

1. Combine the wine, water, olive oil, garlic, bay leaves, thyme, rosemary and lemon juice in a large saucepan. Bring to the boil, add the onions, cover and simmer for 10 minutes.
2. Add the beans and mushrooms and simmer for a further 10 minutes. Remove the bay leaves and rosemary. Serve hot or cold.

PER SERVE: 5 G FAT, 6 G DIETARY FIBRE, 440 KJ (105 CALS)

 SERVES 4

DESSERTS

The ideal dessert is fresh fruit, but occasionally you may want something a bit different. Some diet dessert recipes simply divide a dish into a larger number of portions. That's fine, if you are satisfied by small portions. This chapter looks for ways to produce a genuine low-fat, low-kilojoule dessert.

TIPS

The best dessert is fresh fruit. Buy fruits in season for the best flavour—and usually the best price.

There are a number of recipes in this section for fruit salad. Use them all so that fruit salad does not become a boring dessert that always tastes the same.

Freeze peeled bananas, halved peaches or nectarines, sultana grapes or slices of any kind of melon to use as a dessert substitute on a hot day.

To stop apples or bananas going brown after they are sliced, brush with lemon juice.

BALSAMIC STRAWBERRIES

A delicious way to enjoy strawberries.

1. Combine the sugar and vinegar and stir constantly until the sugar dissolves. Place the strawberries in a bowl, add the vinegar mix and toss gently to combine. Cover and refrigerate for 30 minutes. Serve sprinkled with icing sugar.

1 tbsp dark brown sugar

3 tbsp balsamic vinegar

2 punnets fresh strawberries, hulled

1 tsp icing sugar

PER SERVE: < 1 G FAT, 3 G DIETARY FIBRE, 190 KJ (45 CALS)

 SERVES 4

DRIED FRUIT SALAD

An ideal fruit salad to make in winter.

1 cup water

1 cinnamon stick

6 cloves

4 cardamom pods

1 cup apple or orange juice

250 g dried fruits (apples, apricots, peaches, nectarines, prunes)

1. Heat the water with the cinnamon stick, cloves and cardamom pods. Add the juice and dried fruits, bring to the boil, cover and simmer for 10 minutes. Leave to cool, then chill well. Remove the cinnamon stick, cloves and cardamom pods before serving.

PER SERVE: < 1 G FAT, 5 G DIETARY FIBRE, 630 KJ (150 CALS)

 SERVES 4

MELON BALL FRUIT SALAD

For a special occasion, start with whole melons and use a melon baller to cut round balls of each melon. The leftover portions can be blended with ice for a refreshing drink or used in a melon sorbet (see page 167).

½ medium rockmelon, peeled and diced

½ medium honeydew melon

about 500 g diced watermelon

250 g sultana grapes

2 tbsp orange juice

2 tbsp lime juice

3–4 lime leaves, preferably from a kaffir lime tree (optional)

1. Combine the fruit, juices and lime leaves (if used) and chill well. Just before serving, remove the lime leaves.

PER SERVE: 1 G FAT, 3 G DIETARY FIBRE, 480 KJ (115 CALS)

 SERVES 4

SUMMER FRUIT SALAD

Make this fruit salad at other times of the year by substituting oranges or mandarins for the peaches.

1. Combine the peaches, strawberries, passionfruit, kiwi fruit and orange juice. Chill for one hour. Just before serving, add the banana.

PER SERVE: < 1 G FAT, 13 G DIETARY FIBRE, 670 KJ (160 CALS)

4 peaches, stones removed and diced

1 punnet strawberries

flesh of 6 passionfruit

6 kiwi fruit, peeled and sliced

½ cup orange juice

2 bananas, peeled and sliced

 SERVES 4

STONE FRESH FRUIT SALAD

For a special occasion, serve this fruit salad in a glass bowl set within a larger glass bowl filled with ice.

1. Peel all the fruit and cut the flesh into chunks. Toss well together and chill before serving.

2 mangoes
4 peaches
12 apricots
4 blood plums
250 g cherries

SERVES 4

PER SERVE: 1 G FAT, 9 G DIETARY FIBRE, 810 KJ (195 CALS)

SUMMER BERRY SALAD WITH RASPBERRY SAUCE

This fruit salad is excellent for special occasions or when you want to cook to impress.

300 g frozen raspberries
2 tbsp orange juice
1 tbsp icing sugar
1 punnet strawberries, hulls removed
1 punnet blueberries
1 punnet raspberries
200 g low-fat thick yoghurt

1. Thaw the raspberries and combine with the orange juice and sugar. Blend until smooth. (If you prefer, sieve the sauce as well.)
2. Combine the strawberries, blueberries and raspberries and toss gently together. Place into individual serving dishes and top with the yoghurt. Spoon the raspberry sauce over the top.

PER SERVE: 1 G FAT, 11 G DIETARY FIBRE, 570 KJ (135 CALS)

SERVES 4

AUTUMN FRUIT SALAD

Use mandarins as a delicious alternative to oranges.

1 tbsp flaked almonds
3 oranges, peeled and
all the pith removed
3 pears, peeled
and cored
2 apples, peeled
and cored
¼ cup lemon juice
1 tbsp icing sugar

1. Toast the almonds in a dry frying pan, until golden brown. Shake frequently, taking care they do not burn. Set aside to cool.
2. Slice the oranges, pears and apples and toss gently with the lemon juice. Sprinkle with the icing sugar. Serve in individual dishes. Top with the almonds immediately before serving.

PER SERVE: 2 G FAT, 7 G DIETARY FIBRE, 780 KJ (185 CALS)

 SERVES 4

POACHED VANILLA NECTARINES

Vanilla beans are now available in supermarkets and give a delightful flavour to poached fruit. If desired, substitute apricots, fresh figs or peaches.

1. Place the nectarines, vanilla bean, peach nectar and sherry in a saucepan, bring to the boil, cover and simmer for 5 minutes. Allow to cool, then chill. Remove the vanilla bean just before serving.

PER SERVE: < 1 G FAT, 3 G DIETARY FIBRE, 360 KJ (85 CALS)

8 nectarines
1 vanilla bean, split
down the centre
1 cup peach nectar
2 tbsp sweet sherry

 SERVES 4

PEACHES POACHED IN WHITE WINE

Make this dessert when fresh peaches are in season. It is particularly good with white peaches and is delicious served with fat-reduced fromage frais.

1. Skin the peaches by placing them in a bowl and covering with boiling water. Leave for 1 minute then drain and peel off the skin.
2. Place the peaches in a saucepan with the wine, honey, cinnamon stick and lemon peel. Bring to the boil, cover and simmer for 3 minutes. Leave the peaches in the liquid until cool, then place them in serving dishes, straining the liquid over the top. Chill well before serving.

4 large peaches
1 cup white wine
1 tbsp honey
1 piece of cinnamon stick
1 tsp finely grated lemon peel

PER SERVE: < 1 G FAT, 2 G DIETARY FIBRE, 250 KJ (60 CALS)

SERVES 4

JELLIED BERRIES AND CHERRIES

A great treat on a hot day.

1 punnet strawberries
1 punnet blueberries
500 g fresh cherries
1 tbsp castor sugar
2 tbsp gelatine
1 cup hot water
2 cups dark grape juice

1. Place the berries and cherries into a ring tin or a glass dish.
2. Dissolve the sugar and gelatine in the hot water, add the grape juice, stir well and pour over the berries. Refrigerate until set.

PER SERVE: < 1 G FAT, 4 G DIETARY FIBRE, 860 KJ (205 CALS)

SERVES 4

SUMMER BERRY PUDDING

Summer berry pudding deserves to replace the traditional heavy Christmas pudding that is inappropriate in hot climates. The ideal berries to use are blackberries, mulberries, raspberries and blueberries. You can also include 250 g of sliced strawberries.

400 g can raspberries
1½ kg berries (up to
  half can be
  frozen berries)
10 slices white bread,
  crusts removed
2 tbsp brandy or rum

 SERVES 6

1. Strain the juice from the canned berries into a saucepan and boil until it is reduced to half a cup. Remove from the heat and add the fresh and frozen berries, mixing well, squashing the berries slightly.
2. Line a pudding basin with 6 slices of bread, making sure there are no gaps.
3. Pile the berries into the bread-lined basin and fit more bread on top, again leaving no gaps. Cover the pudding basin with plastic wrap. Weigh down a plate that fits the pudding top exactly. Refrigerate and leave for 24 hours, so that the juices soak into the bread. Turn out when ready to serve.
4. Heat the brandy until hot but not boiling, pour it over the pudding and immediately light the brandy.

PER SERVE: 2 G FAT, 14 G DIETARY FIBRE, 930 KJ (220 CALS)

FROZEN LEMON YOGHURT WITH TOASTED COCONUT AND STRAWBERRIES

An easy dessert that can be made the day before. It looks special if moulded in a heart-shaped tin.

1. Beat the egg whites in a clean dry bowl until soft peaks form. Add the sugar gradually and continue beating until soft peaks again form.
2. Stir in the yoghurt, lemon rind and juice and mix until well combined.
3. Line a 20 cm cake tin with foil, spoon in the yoghurt mixture and freeze for 2 hours or until firm.
4. Toast coconut in a dry frying pan, heating it gently for 1–2 minutes until it turns golden brown. Tip onto a plate and leave to cool.
5. To serve, remove the frozen yoghurt, cut it into 6 wedges and top with coconut. Decorate each serving with strawberries.

PER SERVE: 3 G FAT, 3 G DIETARY FIBRE, 850 KJ (205 CALS)

2 egg whites
½ cup castor sugar
1 kg low-fat
*   natural yoghurt*
finely grated rind of
*   1 lemon*
juice of 1 lemon
cooking foil
½ cup flaked coconut
2 punnets strawberries

 SERVES 6

MANGO AND PAWPAW FREEZE

This is not the same as having a rich ice cream, but it is delicious nevertheless.

2 mangoes, peeled
1 small pawpaw, peeled
    and seeded
2 tbsp lime juice
½ cup castor sugar
500 g low-fat
    natural yoghurt
1 tbsp gelatine
½ cup orange juice

1. Place the mango and pawpaw flesh into a blender or food processor with the lime juice and sugar. Process until smooth. Add the yoghurt and stir to combine.
2. Mix the gelatine and orange juice and dissolve over a gentle heat or in the microwave for 15 seconds. Add the gelatine mix to the mango and pawpaw puree and pour into an ice cream churn, following the manufacturer's directions. If you don't have an ice cream churn, freeze the mixture in a cake tin until almost solid, then beat it in an electric mixer until it is smooth and re-freeze until it is solid.

 SERVES 6

PER SERVE: < 1 G FAT, 3 G DIETARY FIBRE, 740 KJ (175 CALS)

SUMMER BERRY SALAD WITH RASPBERRY SAUCE — SEE PAGE 161

RHUBARB AND APPLE CRUMBLE — SEE PAGE 171

MELON SORBET

Sorbets are wonderfully cooling on a hot day. Scoops of the different sorbets look great together, but you can also use 6 cups of any one melon, if preferred.

1. Puree the rockmelon and pour the puree into a bowl.
2. Puree the honeydew and mint and pour the puree into a bowl.
3. Puree the watermelon and pour the puree into a bowl.
4. In a clean, dry bowl, beat the egg whites until stiff, adding the sugar gradually and continuing to beat until the mixture is thick.
5. Place one third of the egg white mixture on top of each bowl of the three melon purees and fold in carefully until just combined. Place each puree into its own cake tin and freeze until almost solid. Remove each mixture from the freezer, beat well and return to the freezer until solid. Serve a scoop of each sorbet in a chilled glass.

2 cups rockmelon flesh
2 cups honeydew
*   melon flesh*
2–3 mint leaves
2 cups watermelon
*   flesh*
4 egg whites
6 tbsp sugar

 SERVES 6

PER SERVE: < 1 G FAT, 2 G DIETARY FIBRE, 480 KJ (115 CALS)

SPICY FRUITS WITH YOGHURT

It takes only a few minutes to make this dessert, but the flavour improves if you leave it in the fridge an hour before you need it.

1 punnet blueberries
   (or strawberries)
1 orange, peeled
   and sliced
1 grapefruit, peeled,
   pith removed and cut
   into segments
2 bananas, peeled
   and sliced
400 g pie pack apricots
500 g low-fat
   natural yoghurt
1 tsp cinnamon
½ tsp ground
   cardamom
pinch nutmeg

1. Place all the fruits in a bowl.
2. Stir the spices into the yoghurt, pour over the fruit and toss gently together. Allow to stand for an hour, if possible, so that the flavours mingle.

PER SERVE: 1 G FAT, 5 G DIETARY FIBRE, 780 KJ (185 CALS)

 SERVES 4

APRICOT SOUFFLE

A light-as-air dessert that is quick and easy to make.

1. Cook the apricots in the water for 10 minutes. Cool slightly then process in a blender to form a smooth puree.
2. Preheat the oven to 170°C.
3. Beat the egg whites until stiff, add the sugar and continue beating until soft peaks form. Gently fold the apricot puree into the egg whites and spoon into 4 individual souffle dishes. Bake for 15–20 minutes, or until well-risen. Serve at once, as souffles will collapse within a few minutes of being taken out of the oven.

*¾ cup (100 g)
    dried apricots
1 cup water
3 egg whites
2 tbsp castor sugar*

 SERVES 4

PER SERVE: 0 G FAT, 2 G DIETARY FIBRE, 390 KJ (95 CALS)

ORANGE CREPES

Crepes fit in well with a low-fat diet and they're fun to make. Don't toss them too much or they will become leathery.

Crepes
1 cup flour
1 cup skim milk
3 eggs

Orange sauce
¾ cup orange juice
2 tsp cornflour
1 tbsp finely grated
  orange peel
2 tbsp Cointreau or
  Grand Marnier liqueur
3 oranges, peeled, pith
  removed and sliced
light olive oil spray

1. Place the flour, milk and eggs into a bowl or blender and beat until smooth. Leave to stand for at least 30 minutes.
2. Combine 2 tablespoons of the orange juice with the cornflour and stir until smooth. Heat the remaining juice with the orange peel. Add the cornflour mixture and stir until the sauce thickens. Add the liqueur and the orange slices and set aside.
3. Heat a non-stick pan and spray with light olive oil. Pour in about 2 tablespoons of the crepe mixture, swirl to spread and cook until lightly browned. Turn and cook the other side. Place each crepe on a plate and continue cooking the remaining mixture.
4. To serve, fold each crepe in half and top with warm orange sauce.

PER SERVE: 4 G FAT, 4 G DIETARY FIBRE, 1240 KJ (295 CALS)

 SERVES 4

FLAMING BANANAS

An easy dessert to prepare in minutes. If desired, substitute peeled and cored pears for the bananas.

1. Preheat the oven to 180°C. Place the bananas in a shallow ovenproof dish.
2. Combine the sugar, orange peel, juice and cinnamon and spoon over the bananas. Bake for 10 minutes.
3. Warm the rum or brandy in a small saucepan, but do not boil. Remove the bananas from the oven. Light the rum or brandy and pour it quickly over the bananas. Serve at once.

4 small bananas, peeled
  and sliced lengthwise
1 tbsp dark brown sugar
1 tsp finely sliced
  orange peel
¼ cup orange juice
  pinch cinnamon
¼ cup rum or brandy

PER SERVE: 0 G FAT, 4 G DIETARY FIBRE, 790 KJ (190 CALS)

 **SERVES 2**

RHUBARB AND APPLE CRUMBLE

Most crumbles have a high fat content. With less fat, this recipe actually crumbles. Make it in individual dishes for the best results. It tastes great.

1. Place the rhubarb, orange juice and honey in a saucepan, cover and cook over a gentle heat for 5–8 minutes, or until the rhubarb is just cooked. Add the apples and half the cinnamon. Place the mix in 6 individual souffle-style dishes (or use one larger casserole dish).
2. Toast the sunflower seeds in a dry frying pan over a gentle heat, shaking often, until they are golden brown (take care they do not burn). Set aside.
3. Pre-heat the oven to 180°C.
4. Combine the butter, sugar, remaining cinnamon, oats and bran cereal and mix well. Add the sunflower seeds. Spoon the crumble mixture onto the rhubarb and apple and press down gently. Bake in a moderate oven for 30 minutes. Serve hot with low-fat fromage frais or low-fat ice cream.

PER SERVE: 5 G FAT, 8 G DIETARY FIBRE, 920 KJ (220 CALS)

1 bunch rhubarb, cut into 3 cm lengths
2 tbsp orange juice
1 tbsp honey
400 g can pie pack apples
2 tsp cinnamon
1 tbsp sunflower seeds
2 tbsp fat-reduced butter
⅓ cup dark brown sugar
1 cup rolled oats
½ cup processed bran cereal

SERVES 6

PEACHY PANCAKES

Low-fat pancakes are easy to make. Serve them with fruit, ricotta whip (see page 176) or a low-fat fromage frais.

Pancakes
¾ cup wholemeal
    self-raising flour
¾ cup plain flour
¼ tsp baking powder
1 cup skim fat milk
1 tbsp honey
2 eggs
light olive oil spray
cooking foil

Filling
400 g can sliced
    peaches in juice
1 tbsp cornflour
½ tsp cinnamon

 SERVES 4

1. Place the flours, baking powder, milk, honey and eggs in a blender or food processor and process until smooth. Allow to stand for 30 minutes (or refrigerate for up to 12 hours).

2. To prepare the filling, take ¼ cup of liquid from the peaches and blend with the cornflour. Heat the peaches and the remaining juice, then add the cinnamon and the cornflour mixture, stirring constantly until the mixture thickens. Set aside.

3. To make the pancakes, heat a heavy-based non-stick frying pan and spray with light olive oil. Pour about a sixth of the mixture into the pan, swirl to spread it and cook until bubbles appear and the underside is lightly browned. Turn and cook the other side until brown. Stack the cooked pancakes on a plate.

4. Pre-heat the oven to 180°C and spray a shallow ovenproof dish with olive oil.

5. Place a spoonful of filling on each pancake, roll up and place in the ovenproof dish. Cover with foil and reheat in the oven for 5–8 minutes, or until the pancakes are hot. Alternatively, cover the dish with plastic microwave wrap and heat in the microwave for 3–4 minutes. Serve the remaining filling with the pancakes.

PER SERVE: 3 G FAT, 5 G DIETARY FIBRE, 1250 KJ (300 CALS)

BAKED STUFFED APPLES

This is one of the easiest desserts to make. The apples taste best cooked in the oven, but if you're in a hurry the microwave will be fine. Substitute raisins or dried apricots for the prunes, if desired.

1. Pre-heat the oven to 180°C.
2. Core the apples, using an apple corer or a sharp knife. Run a sharp knife around the centre of each apple, making a shallow cut through the skin, which will prevent the apples bursting when they are baked.
3. Stuff the centre of each apple with two prunes and place the apples in an ovenproof dish just large enough to hold them. Pour over the apple juice and bake for 30 minutes. Alternatively, cover the apples loosely with microwave plastic wrap and microwave on High for about 5 minutes, or until the apples are just tender.

4 medium Granny Smith apples
8 pitted prunes
¾ cup apple juice

 SERVES 4

PER SERVE: < 1 G FAT, 4 G DIETARY FIBRE, 500 KJ (120 CALS)

PEACH SPONGE PUDDING

This dessert is great on a cold winter evening.

olive oil spray

2 x 400 g cans pie
   pack peaches

1 tsp cinnamon

2 eggs

⅓ cup castor sugar

2 tbsp lemon juice

1 tsp finely grated
   lemon peel

½ cup self-raising
   flour

1 tbsp cornflour

 SERVES 4

1. Pre-heat the oven to 180°C and spray an ovenproof dish with olive oil spray.
2. Combine the peaches and cinnamon and spread over the base of the prepared dish.
3. Beat the eggs and sugar together until thick and creamy. Add the lemon juice and peel and stir lightly. Sift the flour and cornflour and fold into the egg mixture. Spoon the topping over the peaches and bake for 30 minutes.

PER SERVE: 3 G FAT, 2 G DIETARY FIBRE, 810 KJ (195 CALS)

LEMON SAUCE PUDDING

You can substitute mandarin, grapefruit or orange juice for the lemon in this light sponge-type pudding with its own sauce.

1. Pre-heat the oven to 180°C and spray an ovenproof dish with olive oil spray.
2. Place the water, lemon juice, half the sugar, the flour, egg yolks and skim milk powder in a blender or food processor and process until smooth.
3. Using a clean dry bowl, beat the egg whites until foamy, then add the remaining sugar and continue beating until peaks form. Gently fold the egg whites into the lemon mixture and spoon into the prepared dish. Place the pudding dish in a baking dish, and add water so that it comes halfway up the sides of the pudding dish. Bake for 35–40 minutes, or until set. Serve hot.

olive oil spray
½ cup water
½ cup lemon juice
½ cup castor sugar
2 tbsp plain flour
2 eggs, separated
½ cup skim
  milk powder

 SERVES 4

PER SERVE: 3 G FAT, 0 G DIETARY FIBRE, 840 KJ (200 CALS)

RICOTTA WHIP

This light topping can be used as a substitute for cream.

½ cup dried apricots

½ cup orange juice

1 cup smooth
   ricotta cheese

1. Combine the apricots and orange juice and cook over a gentle heat until the apricots are thick (time will vary according to the dryness of the apricots). Blend until smooth and set aside to cool.
2. Add the ricotta to the apricot and orange mixture and blend until smooth.

 SERVES 6

PER SERVE: 3 G FAT, 1 G DIETARY FIBRE, 360 KJ (85 CALS)

VANILLA SAUCE

Not quite as rich as a good egg custard, this sauce is excellent with poached fruit, fruit crumble or any stewed fruit.

1. Heat 1½ cups of the skim milk and the sugar almost to boiling point.
2. Mix the remaining skim milk, evaporated milk, egg yolk and cornflour and add to the hot milk, stirring continuously until thick.
3. Add the vanilla essence. Serve hot or cold.

PER SERVE: 1 G FAT, 0 G DIETARY FIBRE, 470 KJ (115 CALS)

2 cups skim milk
2 tbsp sugar
¼ cup evaporated skim milk
1 egg yolk
1½ tbsp cornflour
½ tsp vanilla essence

 SERVES 4

BAKING

If you're watching your waistline, it makes sense to restrict cakes to the occasional treat. This is because cakes have a high ratio of kilojoules to nutrients, unlike foods such as fruits, wholegrain bread or low-fat dairy products. But sometimes it's simply nice to have a slice of cake. This section includes cakes that are as low in fat and sugar as flavour allows.

TIPS

Only make cakes when there are enough people present to eat the whole cake.

If you have leftover cake, wrap individual slices and freeze them.

Use non-stick baking paper to line cake tins.

As an alternative to serving cream with cakes, use thick drained yoghurt. To drain yoghurt, place a sieve lined with a new Chux-type absorbent cloth over a basin and fill it with 500 g low-fat yoghurt. Leave it overnight in the refrigerator to drain off the whey.

If you are squeezing oranges, lemons or limes, warm them in the microwave for 20 seconds and the juice will flow more easily.

APPLE CAKE

This is real apple flavour, with dried apples, fresh apples and apple juice. Delicious served warm. Enjoy a small slice!

1. Place the sultanas, apples, apple juice and bicarbonate of soda in a saucepan, bring to the boil and simmer for 2 minutes. Turn off the stove and leave until cool.
2. Preheat the oven to 175°C and line a 20 cm round cake tin with baking paper.
3. Beat the eggs until frothy. Add the fruit mixture, sunflower seeds, sifted flours and half the cinnamon. Spoon into the prepared tin and arrange the apple slices on top. Combine the remaining cinnamon and sugar and sprinkle over the apple. Bake for 40 minutes. Serve warm or allow to cool.

PER SERVE: 4 G FAT, 6 G DIETARY FIBRE, 1160 KJ (275 CALS)

1 cup (170 g) sultanas
1 cup (75 g)
dried apples
1½ cups apple juice
1 tsp bicarbonate
of soda
baking paper
2 eggs
¼ cup (35 g)
sunflower seeds
1 cup wholemeal self-
raising flour
1 cup white self-
raising flour
2 tsp cinnamon
2 fresh apples, cored
and sliced
2 tsp sugar

 SERVES 8

DATE AND PEAR LOAF

A deliciously moist loaf cake made without butter, sugar or eggs.

250 g dates, chopped

200 g dried pears, chopped

450 mL orange juice

baking paper

1½ cups wholemeal plain flour

3 tsp baking powder

1 tsp cinnamon

1 tsp ground cardamom

MAKES 15 SLICES

1. Place the dates and pears in a saucepan, add the orange juice, bring to the boil and cook for 1 minute. Remove from the stove, stir well and cool to lukewarm.

2. Preheat the oven to 175°C and line a 21 x 11 cm loaf tin with baking paper.

3. Sift the flour, baking powder and spices together and add to the fruit mixture, mixing well. Spoon into the prepared tin and bake for 1 hour, or until a skewer inserted into the cake comes out clean. Turn onto a wire rack to cool.

EACH SLICE HAS: < 1 G FAT, 5 G DIETARY FIBRE, 520 KJ (125 CALS)

APPLE CAKE — SEE PAGE 181

FRUIT BROWNIES — SEE P

MANDARIN DATE LOAF

This loaf is not too sweet. Serve it thinly sliced, on its own or spread with low-fat ricotta. Mandarins give an excellent flavour, but you can also use orange juice and peel instead.

1. Place the tea, juice, dates, bicarbonate of soda, cinnamon and mandarin peel in a saucepan and bring to the boil. Cover and simmer for 3 minutes, then turn off the heat and leave until cool.
2. Preheat the oven to 175°C. Line a 22 x 12 cm loaf tin with baking paper.
3. Sift the flour into the date mixture, emptying any husks left over into the mixture as well. Stir well and spoon the mixture into the prepared tin. Sprinkle the poppy seeds on top and press lightly with the back of a spoon so they will stick. Bake for 40 minutes, or until a skewer inserted into the centre comes out clean.

EACH SLICE HAS: 1 G FAT, 3 G DIETARY FIBRE, 310 KJ (75 CALS)

1 cup cold black tea
1 cup mandarin juice
1 cup chopped dates
1 tsp bicarbonate
  of soda
1 tsp cinnamon
2 tsp finely grated
  mandarin peel
baking paper
1 ½ cups wholemeal
  self-raising flour
1 tbsp poppy seeds

 **MAKES 15 SLICES**

ORANGE, MANGO AND APRICOT LOAF

You can whip this loaf up with little effort. It keeps well and tastes good.

200 g dried apricots
1 cup orange and
mango juice
baking paper
1 egg, beaten
1 cup wholemeal
self-raising flour
½ cup self-raising flour
1 tsp cinnamon
½ tsp allspice

1. Place the apricots and orange juice in a saucepan, bring to the boil, cover and simmer for 2 minutes. Remove from the heat and leave until cool.
2. Preheat the oven to 175°C. Line a 21 x 11 cm loaf tin with baking paper.
3. Add the egg, sifted flours and spices to the apricots and mix well. Spoon the mixture into the prepared tin and bake for 40 minutes, or until a skewer inserted into the centre comes out clean.

EACH SLICE HAS: 1 G FAT, 3 G DIETARY FIBRE, 330 KJ (80 CALS)

 **MAKES 15 SLICES**

SCOTTISH OAT CRACKERS

Delicious with fat-reduced cream cheese and slices of apple.

1. Combine the oat bran, oats, sugar, cinnamon and bicarbonate of soda and mix well.
2. Combine the boiling water and butter and stir to dissolve the butter. Add to the oat mixture and mix to make a firm dough, adding a little more water if needed. Form into a sausage shape (about 5–6 cm diameter) and wrap in plastic wrap. Refrigerate for at least 1 and, preferably, 2 hours or longer.
3. Preheat the oven to 160°C and line 2 flat baking trays with baking paper.
4. Cut the oat mixture into thin slices (about 5 mm), place on the baking trays and bake for 15 minutes. Allow to cool and store in an airtight container.

2 cups unprocessed
oat bran
1 cup quick cook
rolled oats
1 tbsp dark brown sugar
1 tsp cinnamon
¼ tsp bicarbonate
of soda
¼ cup boiling water
40 g fat-reduced butter
baking paper

EACH CRACKER HAS: 1 G FAT, 1 G DIETARY FIBRE, 130 KJ (30 CALS)

MAKES 40
APPROXIMATELY

ALMOND BREAD

Nuts are highly nutritious but those trying to lose weight need to exert some caution over quantities. A slice or two of this biscuit gives you a few healthy nuts without taking in too many kilojoules.

1. Preheat the oven to 150°C and line a 20 x 11 cm loaf tin with baking paper.
2. Beat the egg whites until stiff. Gradually add the sugar, beating until the mixture is thick. Add the vanilla essence, almonds and sifted flour. Spoon into the prepared loaf tin and bake for 35 minutes. Turn out and allow to cool on a wire rack, then wrap in foil and leave for 24 hours.
3. Preheat the oven to 150°C again. Slice the loaf as thinly as possible (an electric knife helps) and place the slices on ungreased oven trays. Bake for about 30 minutes, or until the slices are dry and crisp. Do not allow to brown.

baking paper
3 egg whites
½ cup castor sugar
1 tsp vanilla essence
¾ cup blanched almonds
1 cup plain flour
cooking foil

 **MAKES 35 SLICES**

EACH SLICE HAS: 2 G FAT, < 1 G DIETARY FIBRE, 190 KJ (45 CALS)

FRUIT BROWNIES

These are delicious if eaten warm.

1 cup dates

1 cup raisins

1 cup orange juice

baking paper

4 egg whites

2 tbsp castor sugar

½ cup unprocessed
  wheat bran

1 cup self-raising flour

¼ cup cocoa

**CUT INTO 24
SQUARES**

1. Place the dates, raisins and orange juice in a saucepan, bring to the boil, cover and simmer for 2 minutes. Remove from the heat and leave until lukewarm.

2. Preheat the oven to 175°C. Line a 27 x 18 cm shallow cake tin (or use a 23 cm square tin) with baking paper.

3. Beat the egg whites until stiff, gradually adding the sugar. Fold the egg whites into the fruit mixture, then add the bran, sifted flour and cocoa, stirring gently until combined. Spoon into the prepared tin and bake for 30 minutes.

EACH SQUARE HAS: < 1 G FAT, 2 G DIETARY FIBRE, 290 KJ (70 CALS)

LOW-FAT CHOCOLATE CAKE

This bears little resemblance to a rich mud cake, but then they have over 80 g of fat per slice. This one has less than 1 gram.

1. Preheat the oven to 160°C and line a 20 cm round cake tin with baking paper.
2. Place the prunes, apple juice and bicarbonate of soda in a saucepan, bring to the boil, turn off the heat, cover and leave until cool. Once cool, puree until smooth.
3. Sift the flour and cocoa and stir into the cooled prune puree.
4. Beat the egg whites until stiff, adding the sugar gradually. Fold half the egg whites into the prune mixture and then fold in the remaining egg whites. Spoon into the prepared cake tin and bake for 35 minutes or until a cake skewer inserted into the middle comes out clean. Cool on a rack and just before serving, sieve the icing sugar over the top.

baking paper
100 g pitted prunes
¾ cup apple juice
¼ tsp bicarbonate
  of soda
1 cup self-raising flour
½ cup cocoa powder
4 egg whites
½ cup castor sugar
2 tsp icing sugar

 SERVES 8

EACH SLICE HAS: 1 G FAT, 2 G DIETARY FIBRE, 660 KJ (160 CALS)

COOKING
TO IMPRESS

A typical dinner party menu of two or three courses can easily contain 120 g fat and around 8000 kJ. That's why people who eat out or entertain a lot are often overweight. Eating is fun and the following menus should allow you to enjoy good food for a fraction of the fat and kilojoules. Each menu has also been chosen to represent minimum preparation time.

3 COURSE DINNER PARTY FOR 6

ENTREE
Sesame prawns and asparagus (see page 126)

MAIN COURSE
Roast vegetable lasagne (see page 36)

DESSERT
Frozen lemon yoghurt with toasted coconut and strawberries (see page 165)

TOTAL FOR MEAL PER SERVE: 15 G FAT, 15 G FIBRE, 2730 KJ (655 CALS)

3 COURSE DINNER PARTY FOR 4

ENTREE
Warm spiced pear salad with rocket and walnuts (see page 24)

MAIN COURSE
Chicken in pomegranate molasses (see page 120)

Greek-style beans (see page 155)

Roasted tomatoes (see page 155)

DESSERT
Poached vanilla nectarines (see page 162)

TOTAL FOR MEAL PER SERVE: 16 G FAT, 17 G FIBRE, 2490 KJ (595 CALS)

Alternative 2 course meal: omit the entree

TOTAL FOR MEAL PER SERVE: 12 G FAT, 11 G FIBRE, 1800 KJ (430 CALS)

2 COURSE DINNER PARTY FOR 4

MAIN COURSE
Grilled lamb with red capsicum sauce (see page 121)

Potato souffle (see page 145)

Steamed green beans

DESSERT
Jellied berries and cherries (see page 163)

TOTAL FOR MEAL PER SERVE: 9 G FAT, 12 G FIBRE, 2640 KJ (630 CALS)

Barbecued dinner for 4

Main course

Barbecued ocean trout with dill sauce (see page 92)

Barbecued asparagus (see page 82)

Barbecued mushrooms (see page 81)

Cherry tomatoes

Dessert

Melon sorbet (see page 167)

Total for meal per serve: 10 g fat, 9 g fibre, 1830 kJ (445 Cals)

Another easy barbecue for 4

Main course

Brandied chicken with lime, honey and rosemary (see page 85)

Barbecued fennel (see page 82)

Green salad

Dessert

Stone fresh fruit salad (see page 161)

Total for meal per serve: 9 g fat, 17 g fibre, 2300 kJ (550 Cals)

Quick dinner for 4

Main course

Prawn and orange pasta (see page 41)

Green salad with balsamic vinegar

Dessert

Summer berry salad with raspberry sauce (see page 161)

Total for meal per serve: 3 g fat, 24 g fibre, 2540 kJ (605 Cals)

DINNER FOR 2

MAIN COURSE

Baked chicken with lemon and caramelised onions (see page 118)

Honeyed ginger carrots (see page 147)

Sesame snow peas and beans (see page 151)

DESSERT

Balsamic strawberries (see page 159)

TOTAL PER SERVE: 12 G FAT, 16 G FIBRE, 1620 KJ (385 CALS)

LIGHT DINNER FOR 2

MAIN COURSE

Warm Thai chicken salad (see page 117)

Per serve: 7 g fat, 5 g dietary fibre, 840 kJ (200 Cals)

DESSERT

Melon ball fruit salad (see page 160)

Per serve: 1 g fat, 3 g dietary fibre, 480 kJ (115 Cals)

TOTAL PER SERVE: 8 G FAT, 8 G FIBRE, 1320 KJ (315 CALS)

CONVERSIONS

The recipes in this book use the Australian measures.

▨ OVEN TEMPERATURES

	Fahrenheit	Celsius
Very slow	250°F	120°C
Slow	275°–300°F	140°–150°C
Moderately slow	325°F	160°C
Moderate	350°F	180°C
Moderately hot	375°F	190°C
Hot	400°–450°F	200°–230°C
Very hot	475°–500°F	250°–260°C

▨ MASS (WEIGHT)

Imperial	Metric
½ oz	15 g
1 oz	30 g
2 oz	60 g
3 oz	90 g
4 oz (¼ lb)	125 g
5 oz	155 g
6 oz	180 g
7 oz	220 g
8 oz (½ lb)	250 g
9 oz	280 g
10 oz	315 g
11 oz	345 g
12 oz (¾ lb)	375 g
13 oz	410 g
14 oz	440 g
15 oz	470 g
16 oz (1 lb)	500 g (0.5 kg)
24 oz (1½ lb)	750 g
32 oz (2 lb)	1000 g (1kg)
3 lb	1500 g

▨ LIQUID

Imperial	Cup	Metric
1 fl oz		30 mL
2 fl oz	¼ cup	60 mL
4 fl oz	½ cup	90 mL
5 fl oz (¼ pint)	⅔ cup	150 mL
6 fl oz	¾ cup	200 mL
8 fl oz	1 cup	250 mL
10 fl oz (½ pint)	1¼ cups	300 mL
12 fl oz	1½ cups	375 mL
14 fl oz	1¾ cups	425 mL
16 fl oz	2 cups	500 mL
20 fl oz (1 pint)	2½ cups	600 mL

▨ STANDARDS

Cup	Spoon
¼ cup = 60 mL	¼ teaspoon = 1.25 mL
⅓ cup = 80 mL	½ teaspoon = 2.5 mL
½ cup = 125 mL	1 teaspoon = 5 mL
1 cup = 250 mL	1 tablespoon = 20 mL

Different countries use different tablespoon sizes

In Australia:

1 tablespoon = 20 mL or 4 teaspoons

In New Zealand:

1 tablespoon = 15 mL or 3 teaspoons

In the United Kingdom and the United States:

1 tablespoon = 15 mL or 3 teaspoons

RECIPE INDEX